Dedication

I dedicate this book to Braden, Bethany, and Katelyn, who were on my heart as I wrote this book, and also to all the children in the world who suffer emotionally because they lacked the bonding relationships God intended when children are welcomed by loving parents. Your courage and bravery in the midst of your successes and failures make me want to cheer and cry at the same time. And to all the moms of these children, whose selfless love often goes unnoticed. May God bless you for your unfailing compassion and commitment to the children who need you the most.

"The Spirit of the Lord is upon me, because he hath anointed me to preach the gospel to the poor; he hath sent me to heal the brokenhearted, to preach deliverance to the captives, and recovering of sight to the blind, to set at liberty them that are bruised" (Luke 4:18).

Table of Contents

Note From the Author — vii

CHAPTER 1 An Orphanage at Home — 1

CHAPTER 2 Sweeper's Disease — 11

CHAPTER 3 Tanisha — 31

CHAPTER 4 Thankful for Snow? — 43

CHAPTER 5 The End of the Honeymoon — 57

CHAPTER 6 A Deep Black Hole — 77

CHAPTER 7 A Child Who Has Never Been Loved — 101

CHAPTER 8 A Glimmer of Hope — 121

CHAPTER 9 I'm Just a Bad Girl — 133

CHAPTER 10 God's Hands and Feet — 149

CHAPTER 11 The Forgivingest People in the World — 169

CHAPTER 12 Dollhouse Trauma — 185

CHAPTER 13 Birthday Misunderstanding — 205

CHAPTER 14 Too Much Excitement — 225

CHAPTER 15 Hugs for Mother — 247

CHAPTER 16 My Heart Says I Love You — 265

Acknowledgments — 281

Reactive Attachment Disorder — 283

Note From the Author

Adoption has been dear to my heart almost from before I can remember. It was a secret dream I carried in my heart that, for some reason, I shared with no one. I loved the books *The Family God Gave* and *The Family Nobody Wanted*. I knew I wanted to adopt some day. My dreams were not noble ones. I only wanted a family—a sweet, chubby, brown-skinned baby I could call my own.

When my husband Craig and I got married and it seemed as if we would be called to walk the path of infertility, my heart quickly turned to adoption. It wasn't long until my husband began to dream along with me.

I considered myself blessed beyond measure when less than two years after we were married, we traveled to Liberia, West Africa, to adopt not just one baby, but twin boys! One was chubby; the other was skinny, but I loved them both. Thus began our journey into the reality of adoption.

We were fairly isolated during those first years as an adoptive family. We didn't know many other families who had adopted children, but we did the normal things for our babies. We fed them, we clothed them, and we lavished our love upon them. Our skinny baby filled out, and soon we had two sturdy, healthy little boys.

When our twins, Brett and Brady, were not quite three years old, a blonde, blue-eyed little girl was born to us, making us the parents of three children, ages two and under.

By the time Lindsay was two, we longed for another baby. Once more we started the adoption process, and after two years of seeming impossibilities, God blessed us with a tiny African-American girl we named Shaniya. Now we had two girls and two boys.

But the scales tipped in favor of the girls when almost four years later, Tiffany was born to us. More girls in the family gave us more emotions and more tears, but also more girlish giggles.

With the addition of each child came a growing awareness of our limitations as parents. While God's Word always applies to child training, children's personalities and sensitivities can be quite different, even in the same family. We parents take that into consideration as we apply God's principles in bringing up our biological children. We found we needed to be even more discerning with our adopted children who were emotionally affected by the dark world they had been born into. We began to see more clearly the effects that our sinful, broken world has on innocent children. We realized that prenatal exposure to drugs and alcohol, domestic violence, neglect, and trauma of every kind imaginable has a devastating impact on many children born today. Children from such settings are often emotionally hurt and broken. We found ourselves ill-equipped to deal with the damage that had been done before our adopted children had come to us.

Seeking to connect with other adoptive families, we started attending adoption picnics and adoption fellowship meetings. We learned we weren't the only ones struggling to understand the needs of our children. We also realized that many other families struggled with a lack of understanding from their churches and extended families.

Many devastating results stem from prenatal and early childhood trauma. The normal emotional attachment between a child and its biological mother may be poorly formed, nonexistent, or broken. In severe cases, children may be diagnosed with Reactive Attachment Disorder (RAD). Children with attachment difficulties may resist emotional attachment to anyone, especially the mother or other primary caregiver in their lives. They may build an emotional shell around themselves as protection from further hurt. They may avoid closeness to those who are responsible for their care, yet create superficial relationships with people outside the family they live with. To family and friends who don't live with them, they may appear sweet, smiling, and affectionate. This may be how they have learned to feel in control of potentially hurtful situations. Those looking on may find it hard to believe that such a small, cute child could cause the havoc described by foster or adoptive parents who have chosen to bring them into their homes.

Not every foster or adopted child suffers from RAD, but the effects of trauma in any child can cause misunderstandings in home and church life if people are not aware of the damage it can do.

My goal for this story is to take you into the home of an adoptive family and build a bridge of understanding between churches, communities, and the parents of troubled children. If you understand the effects of early childhood trauma, you may be able to draw more accurate conclusions when you see a seemingly sweet child being "overprotected" by a weary mother. When you observe an angry, out-of-control child, you may be able to see beyond the surface to the wounded places in her heart rather than place blame on her parents' shoulders. If this story can generate greater compassion and understanding support for foster and adoptive families in our extended families and churches, it will accomplish the goal I aimed for.

Because times and terminology change, new labels for childhood attachment difficulties in children may be in effect by the time you read this book. But as long as young children's lives are disrupted and damaged by violence, neglect, trauma, and prenatal exposure to drugs and alcohol, the emotional effects such as those displayed by Tanisha in this story will continue to occur.

Because I am an adoptive mother in the middle of raising five children, you may wonder if Tanisha is one of my own children. The answer is no. Tanisha's character is a composite of several children, and her behavior is taken from what is typical of a child diagnosed with RAD.

The only child in the story who is very much like one of my children is Robbie. During the time I wrote most of this story, Robbie and Shaniya were close to the same age; therefore, Robbie's personality became very like our daughter Shaniya's.

CHAPTER ONE

An Orphanage at Home

It was a cold evening in January as Twila Hammond dried the last of the supper dishes and placed the kettle in the cupboard where it belonged. She had offered to finish up the dishes to give her older sister Marilyn more time to study for a science test. Twila couldn't honestly say she loved to work—least of all dishes—but at thirteen, it wasn't the trial it had been when she was younger.

As Twila glanced around the kitchen to see if she had forgotten anything, she remembered that she hadn't swept the floor. It wasn't important to her, but she knew Marilyn never considered the kitchen work finished until the floor was swept. As Twila pulled the broom from the closet and began swishing the dirt to a pile in the middle of the room, her mind wandered to the stories Dad had told at the supper table. He was doing some painting for an older couple who were full of stories. Mr. Becker and his wife had spent twenty-four years teaching Native American children in remote villages of Alaska before they had retired and moved back to Wisconsin where they had grown up.

Twila's broom moved slower as her mind went over the details Dad had related. *Maybe I could teach school someday,* she thought. *Not just in the United States, but some place far away. Alaska?* She rejected the idea. It was too cold there and from what she had heard, the sun hardly shone in the wintertime. She wanted to go somewhere warm. *Maybe Costa Rica—or India!*

The broom had totally stopped now. Twila cupped her hand over the end of the broom handle, propped her chin on top, and stared dreamily down at the floor. *Yes, India. That's where I want to go!* Twila envisioned a mud hut schoolroom, with a thatched roof and rows of darling dark-eyed children with jet black hair.

"Cotcha!" Twila jumped and looked up to see Marilyn grinning at her from the doorway. "So what were you dreaming about this time?" Marilyn wondered.

Twila flushed a little and started sweeping again. She was known as the daydreamer of the family. Although in recent years she had tried hard to overcome her habit, she still occasionally got caught. She looked at Marilyn and said saucily, "Wouldn't you like to know!"

But the thrill of her daydream had taken hold of her, and she couldn't quite resist telling Marilyn. "I was thinking about those stories Dad told about the Beckers teaching school in Alaska. I think it would be so much fun to teach school somewhere far away. Not in Alaska, but maybe some place like India."

Marilyn pulled out a chair and sat down. She propped her elbows on the table and said enthusiastically, "I thought too it sounded like fun to teach school in some foreign place! But I think I'd rather go to Africa or South America." She paused. "But if I went to Africa, I'd rather start an orphanage for abandoned babies than teach school."

Twila's eyes lit up. "Hey, I like that idea! Can I come with you? Let's you and I both go to Africa or India or somewhere and start an orphanage when we grow up."

Marilyn grinned. "We can spend our lives taking care of orphan children and be two old ladies working together." She stood up suddenly. "But if I'm going to study for my science test, I'd better get with it. I came to the kitchen for a drink, not to talk about starting orphanages."

Twila put the broom away. "It sure would be fun though. I hope I can do something like that someday."

Marilyn drank her water and tipped her cup upside down in the sink. She said seriously, "I'm sure it would be fun and interesting. But it would be an awfully big responsibility."

Marilyn went back to studying her test while Twila grabbed a book and wandered into the living room. She curled up at one end of the couch and began reading, her dreams momentarily forgotten.

Her three younger sisters lay sprawled on the floor playing a game of Trouble. Their laughter and friendly competition made it hard for Twila to concentrate on her book. She finally gave up and sat soaking in the peace and tranquility of the evening.

In the office, Dad was talking on the phone with a work customer. In the rocker nearby, Mother sat holding three-year-old Robbie. She walked her fingers up his back and said, "Spiders crawling up your back!" He giggled when Mother tickled him. He loved the little games Mother played with him.

Robbie wrapped his arms around Mother's neck and said, "I love you, Mama."

Mother gave him a squeeze in return. "I love you too."

Robbie laughed again and replied, "I love you too, too, too!"

Twila's gaze drifted across the room to where her little sisters were playing. Rita, Connie, and Suzanne were stair-stepped in age and size. Rita was nine, Connie was ten, and Suzanne was eleven.

With the palm of her hand, Connie pushed down on the bubble of the Trouble game to shake the dice. "Oh, good!" she cheered in delight when she got the number she was hoping for.

Twila had a sudden insight. *Connie's the only one with whom Mother never had the chance to play all those little baby games she's playing with Robbie now.* It was hard to believe. It seemed as though Connie had been with them forever.

Connie and Robbie were grandchildren to Mrs. Weatherby, a next-door neighbor to the church school that the Hammond girls attended. Almost two years ago, Mrs. Weatherby had fallen and broken her hip. When she was no longer able to take care of her grandchildren, Social Services placed Robbie in the care of the Hammond family. Connie had gone to stay with another family who was licensed to foster older children.

The Hammonds were delighted to have Robbie join their family, but their hearts had gone out to Connie, who was now separated from her little brother. Dad and Mother had gotten their paperwork updated so Connie could come to live with them. Just two months ago, they had gone before the judge, and now Connie's and Robbie's adoptions were complete.

Adoption day had been an exciting day for everyone in the family, but especially for Connie. She was pleased to finally be a Hammond and thrilled when Dad and Mother gave her the middle name of Ann. *Ann* was part of Mother's name, so it was special to Connie. It seemed to make her feel connected to Mother. Now on every available scrap of paper, Connie would proudly scrawl her full name, *Consuela Ann Hammond.*

There were laughter and groans from the girls as Suzanne triumphantly moved her last button home and finished the game. Laughing and talking, the girls put the game pieces back in the box, and Rita put the game away.

With a sigh, Suzanne leaned back against a chair and announced, "What we need is some excitement around here."

"By all the noise you girls were making, I would think you had enough excitement just playing that game," observed Mother.

Suzanne tipped one of Robbie's tractors upside down and gave one of its wheels a spin. "Oh, I'm not talking about that kind of fun. I'm talking about foster children excitement. Mother, haven't you gotten any calls about a child needing care? It's been weeks since we've had anyone!"

Rita twirled the end of her curly blonde braid around her finger and said wistfully, "I wish they'd bring us a baby again. Robbie's so big, he's not a baby anymore."

Suzanne grinned. "Well, I wish Wyatt could come back again. He sure livened things up around here."

"He definitely did," Mother replied. "But I'm glad he can be back with his father. Mrs. Gunther says it's going well for him there. And no, we haven't gotten any calls in quite a while. It would be nice to have a little one again, but I think the Lord knows we need these quieter in-between times too. We can catch our breath and get prepared for the next child."

Somehow, though the Hammonds had not really planned on it, they had started taking in older children as well as babies after their paperwork had been updated to allow Connie to live with them. In the last eighteen months, several children of different ages and needs had come through their home. Wyatt, a lively six-year-old, had been with them the longest. They would have been glad to have him become a part of their family, but though they missed Wyatt, they were happy he and his dad could be reunited.

One time, two-month-old twins had come to stay with them. For once the girls felt as though there were enough babies to go around. During the day Mother changed diapers, rocked babies, and fed bottles. In the afternoon the girls would rush home from school to help take care of Robbie and the babies and assist Mother in catching up with the housework. Though it was a busy time, the girls had loved having three babies in the house.

Some of the children stayed only a few days, some a few weeks, and others several months. And then to the joy of the Hammonds, there were Connie and Robbie, who had become a permanent part of the family.

"What happened to Chad, Mother?" questioned Rita. "Didn't he have autism?"

"Yes," replied Mother. "But he's happy with his grandmother and responding well to the treatment program he's on. I heard he's even starting to talk."

"Oh, good!" exclaimed Rita. "I felt so sorry for him when he would hide behind the couch and cover his ears."

"Yes, some noises certainly bothered him," agreed Mother. "I'm glad he's getting such good care from his grandmother."

Marilyn had finished studying. She came into the living room and sat down beside Twila. After listening for a few moments to the chatter, Marilyn leaned over and said quietly to Twila, "I don't think we need to go anywhere far away to work in an orphanage. We already live in one."

Twila grinned. "Oh, this is just giving us preparation for later!" she answered. Marilyn smiled and nodded.

Just then there was a crunch of gravel as a car pulled in the lane. Connie ran to the window. "It's Grandma Hammond!" she announced. "Is that exciting enough for you, Suzanne?"

Suzanne grinned. "It'll do! Come, Robbie. Let's go to the door and tell Grandma to come in."

Robbie slid down from Mother's lap and ran after Suzanne. Connie and Rita trailed along behind. "Hello, girls! Hello, Robbie!" Grandma greeted as she stepped in the door. Talking all at once, the children escorted her to the living room.

"Hi, Grandma," said Marilyn. "Here, you can sit over here." She jumped up from the couch and removed some books from a chair.

Grandma sank into the chair. "Thank you, dear!" She surveyed her surroundings. "My, you must have all been working hard today. Your house is shining clean."

"We housecleaned the living room today," offered Twila.

Mother smiled. "I'm very blessed! With two teenage girls in the house, the work just disappears. And the three younger girls are learning to do the work that Twila and Marilyn were doing a few years ago."

Rita sighed. "But things don't stay clean very long, 'cause Robbie comes along and messes things up right after we just got everything cleaned."

Grandma chuckled. "That's a pretty typical problem when you have a three-year-old in the house."

"So, Twila, have you done any more painting or drawing lately?" Grandma wondered.

Twila nodded. "I finished painting some flowers on an old vase I found in the cupboard. That was awhile ago, though. Now I've started drawing a picture of Dad at work. I still can't draw people very well, and I'm having trouble getting the lines angled properly to make the ceiling and walls look realistic."

"Would you mind showing it to me?" asked Grandma. "Maybe I could give you a few tips from the drawing class I took several years ago. Well," Grandma corrected herself with a chuckle, "that was back when Uncle Jerry still was a boy at home, so I guess it was more like fifteen years ago."

Twila handed her drawing to Grandma, and Grandma studied the picture of Dad perched on a scaffold, painting a ceiling. "You've done very well, Twila. Even if I didn't know this was a picture of your dad, I'd still think it looks like him. But you're right. You're having some trouble with these lines. I think you need to slant them a little lower, not quite so high." Grandma demonstrated with her finger. As they discussed the artwork, Grandma gave Twila additional suggestions.

"Keep practicing, and you'll get it figured out," Grandma encouraged, handing the paper back to Twila. "One more question though," she added. "Why do you have your dad working so

high up on that scaffolding? It makes me lightheaded just thinking of being that far off the ground!"

Twila laughed. "I guess because that's what Dad was doing the
day we stopped in at the job to see him. He was painting, and I
decided to draw him while he was working."

Twila went to put her paper away. Robbie leaned over the arm
of Grandma's chair, his dark eyes animated as he told her big stories of how he was going to go to work with Dad and help paint.
Grandma put an arm around him and squeezed him close. "You're
getting to be a big boy. Before you know it, you'll be big enough
to go to work too."

Grandma looked over his head at Mother. "He sure talks a
lot, and very clearly for his age. I'm getting worried about Jerry's
twins. They'll be three in July, and they still don't say very many
words. I talked to Julia about it, and she doesn't seem concerned. I
guess she taught special ed students enough years that she should
know what's typical and what isn't. It just seems strange for Jerry
and Julia to have quiet children after a talker like Ricky."

Grandma leaned back in her chair. "Ricky has grown up a lot
in the last couple years, but he still likes to talk, that's for sure. He
comes over almost every day and catches me up on everything. I
enjoy it! It keeps me from feeling lonely. I thank God many times
for the blessing of being able to live in my own little house right
in Jerry's yard."

"Julia must be feeling pretty busy now that they have a new
baby," Mother commented. "How is she doing? I should call her
and see if she needs one of the girls to help her again."

"You'll have to ask her how she feels about more help. It's only
one baby this time. I think after having twins the last time, this
addition feels pretty easy to them. It helps that baby Kendra sleeps
well at night and is content during the day. But Julia is still a busy
mama." Grandma pulled a handkerchief out of her apron pocket

and polished her glasses. She held them up to the light to make sure they were clean.

"Did you go to visit Uncle Tim's last weekend?" wondered Marilyn. "I noticed you weren't in church Sunday and then Dad said that's where you were planning to go."

Grandma tucked her handkerchief back in her pocket. "Yes, I did, Marilyn. And that reminds me. Guess what I have at my house, Robbie!"

Robbie thought for a moment. "A kitty?" he asked.

"Pretty close," said Grandma. "It's a puppy."

"A puppy!" exclaimed Connie. "Where did you get a puppy?"

Grandma chuckled. "When I was visiting at Uncle Tim's, your cousin Steve happened to mention to me that his friend had a puppy he was trying to sell. So I decided I wanted to see it. We haven't had a dog around the place since Ricky's got run over last year. So Monday morning before I left, Tim and Steve took me over to check into buying this pup. Steve's friend Jim took us out behind the garage to see him. He's a cute little fellow with a curled-up tail. He's kind of a bluish-gray color."

"What kind of dog is he?" wondered Marilyn.

"Jim called him an Alaskan malamute. I decided I wanted him so I bought him. As we were leaving, I told Steve's friend, 'Now, I got him from you, so I'm going to call the puppy Jim.'" Grandma chuckled again. "Jim got a funny look on his face. I don't think he knew whether to be pleased or not."

Dad had finished his phone call and came into the living room just as Grandma was telling her story. "That dog will be digging in your flower beds next spring," Dad said. He sat down by Marilyn on the other end of the couch and stretched his long legs in front of him. The talk flowed on as Grandma and Twila's parents discussed church events, family news, and the latest comfort top Grandma was working on.

Twila sat drowsily in her corner of the couch listening to the contented murmur of the younger children and the hum of adult conversation. The warmth of family love wrapped around her. The peace and serenity of the evening made her feel as though she would never trade places with anyone in the world for her own special spot in this family. Right now she never wanted to leave. Not even to work in an orphanage in India.

CHAPTER TWO

Sweeper's Disease

Twila stood outside the back door and took a deep breath. A late January thaw the day before had turned the winter air suddenly balmy. The snow was rapidly disappearing. Twila looked wistfully to the edge of the yard where the trail began that meandered through the woods behind their house. A few weeks earlier when she had tried to take a walk, the snowdrifts had been so deep that all she had gotten was boots full of snow. She had given up, but promised herself that when there was less snow, she would try again.

But she didn't have time to daydream. She purposefully picked up the buckets of water and feed and made her way out to the henhouse. There was no time for a walk now. The chickens must be fed, and after breakfast it would be time to leave for school. Maybe this afternoon she'd be able to slip back for a stroll through the woods.

Twila made short work of the chicken chores and headed back to the house.

That afternoon when school was out, Twila grabbed her lunch box from the shelf, and laughing and talking with a group of school friends, she stepped out the door. Mother was already there, waiting for them in the van. As they drove out the school lane, Mother said, "Aunt Julia could use help for a couple of hours this afternoon. Twila, I told her I'd drop you off after school."

"Oh, good!" Twila responded. "I like helping Aunt Julia."

"That's not fair," grumbled Suzanne good-naturedly. "I wish I was old enough to do fun stuff like that. And you'll get to hold the new baby too."

"I suppose I will," replied Twila. "But I'll be there to work, not just to hold the baby."

"Well, make sure you do then, and don't be leaning on your broom staring into space," Marilyn teased.

Twila wrinkled her nose at Marilyn. "Oh, don't worry!" she shot back. "I'm all caught up on my thinking right now!"

They were nearing Uncle Jerry's when Robbie suddenly exclaimed, "Mama, Mama, don't forget to stop at Yellow Buttons! You said you wanted to get some honey."

For a moment Mother looked puzzled. Then she chuckled. "Oh, you mean Yolanda Barton! It's a good thing you reminded me, or I would have forgotten to stop for a jar of honey."

She slowed down and pulled into the Bartons' lane. On one side lay a field that in the summer grew clover. Near its edge sat a long row of white beehives.

Robbie leaned out of his car seat. "I want to see some bees," he said.

"It's still winter, Robbie," said Connie wisely. "The bees don't come out when it's cold."

Robbie looked disappointed. "Well, I'm still going to check."

When they arrived at Mrs. Barton's house, Mother got out of the van and went into the old milk house that Mrs. Barton had converted into a little store where she sold honey, maple syrup, and cheese. A short time later she came out with a jar of honey.

When they got to Uncle Jerry's, Twila hurried into the house. Ricky and the twins, Janice and Justin, were already sitting at the table eating an afternoon snack when she entered the kitchen.

"Welcome!" said Aunt Julia. "Why don't you sit down and have some cookies with us before you start working?"

Twila bit into a molasses cookie and listened as Ricky told stories about his day at school. The more Ricky talked, the more dramatic his stories became. Twila suspected it was partly because she was there. "I freed three people when we were skating at noon recess," Ricky bragged. "That's because I'm the fastest skater in my grade. I can *easy* skate faster than Timmy, and he's *way* bigger than me!"

Aunt Julia said firmly, "Ricky, I think it's time you stop talking about yourself and talk about something else. As big as your stories are getting, you soon won't be telling the truth anymore."

Ricky gave Aunt Julia an injured look. "I wasn't telling lies. I was telling a parable. It's okay to tell parables. The Bible does."

Twila choked back her laughter and grabbed her glass. She jumped up and turned to fill it with water at the kitchen sink. But Aunt Julia did not sound amused as she informed Ricky of the difference between exaggeration and parables. Then, since Ricky had finished his snack, she sent him off to do his chicken chores and feed the cats.

Aunt Julia turned to Twila with a small sigh and a twinkle in her eye. "It's a good thing I had twelve years of teaching experience or I would *not* be able to keep ahead of that boy," she said with a rueful laugh. "A parable indeed!"

She picked up a paper from the kitchen counter. "Here's what I was hoping we could get done while you're here. I thought it might help if I made a list." She handed it to Twila.

"I'm going to start on supper while the baby's sleeping," Aunt Julia went on. "I'd like if you could fold those baskets of laundry and if you have time, clean the bathroom. I didn't have time to do it on Saturday. Oh, and it'd be nice if the kitchen and dining room floors could be swept too. I was taking care of the baby this morning, and the twins made a big mess of the play dough when I wasn't watching. Do what you can, and we'll see how much we have time for."

Aunt Julia washed Janice's and Justin's faces and told them they could go play. They slid from their stools and followed Twila into the living room where she was folding clothes. As she worked, Twila tried to keep them entertained so Aunt Julia could fix supper. The twins insisted on helping her fold washcloths. Twila thought it was fun to have their help even though it slowed her down.

When they went to put the folded laundry away, Justin dropped his stack of washcloths. "Uh-oh!" he exclaimed. Gathering them all up in his chubby arms, he followed Twila to the bathroom where she quickly refolded them and put them away. She had just finished putting away the last of the laundry when Ricky burst into the house.

"Mom! Mom!" he yelled. "We got a whole dozen of eggs today."

Aunt Julia peered into Ricky's egg bucket. "The chickens must be laying more since the weather warmed up. Take your boots off and be sure to hang up your coat before you wash the eggs," she said.

Twila got the broom and started sweeping the kitchen, and Ricky went to do as bidden. Then he took his bucket of eggs to the sink to wash them.

A few minutes later he called, "Mom, look what I can do!" Twila was startled to see Ricky juggling three eggs with surprising skill.

Aunt Julia looked up from the stove. "Ricky!" she gasped. "You're going to break one."

Before she finished speaking, an egg slipped from Ricky's fingers and fell with a splat. He tried to catch the other two, but he fumbled again, and a second egg also fell and broke. Gooey egg puddled on the floor amid the pieces of shattered shell.

Ricky looked down at the broken eggs remorsefully. "I don't know how it happened. I didn't mean to. They just slipped out of my fingers."

"I'm sure you didn't mean to," said Aunt Julia. "But you know better than to juggle eggs. Better clean up your mess and put the rest of the eggs in the refrigerator."

Ricky obeyed and then went to the living room to play with the twins.

Aunt Julia stirred vigorously, whisking together salad dressing ingredients. "My oldest sister came to visit recently," she told Twila, "and her sixteen-year-old son taught Ricky how to juggle. Now Ricky juggles everything from potatoes to little toys. Last evening when I told him to set the table, he was juggling cups. Now today it's eggs, of all things." Aunt Julia shook her head, but Twila caught the fond look in her eyes. No one would ever guess that Ricky was her stepson. Ricky's mother had died, and Uncle Jerry had married Julia when Ricky was six years old.

Twila admired Aunt Julia. She always seemed to have the right mixture of patience and firmness. Twila put the broom away and started on another job. She was able to clean the bathroom and get a few other things done for Aunt Julia before Dad stopped in on his way home from work to pick her up.

Aunt Julia surveyed her now tidy house and exclaimed, "Thank you so much for coming, Twila! You don't know what a lift it gave me."

Twila shrugged. "You're welcome, but I really didn't do that much."

"Oh, yes, you did!" replied Aunt Julia. "With all the interruptions, it would have taken me much longer to do it myself. You got a lot done, and you kept the children happy too!"

Before climbing into the truck where Dad was waiting, Twila turned and waved at Janice and Justin who were watching from the living room window.

When Dad and Twila got home, Mother had just hung up the phone. She turned to the rest of the family with a twinkle in her eyes. "Well, Suzanne, I guess you got your wish. And yes, Rita, we're getting a baby this time!"

"Oh, so that was Mrs. Gunther who called!" squealed Connie. "Is it a boy or a girl?"

"Yes, it was Mrs. Gunther. And it's a little boy this time. She's bringing him over at four o'clock tomorrow afternoon. She says this is short-term, so the baby will probably be staying only a week or two. His name is Dustin, and he's four months old."

"So he'll be pretty little yet," Marilyn commented.

"I was hoping we'd be able to keep him longer," Suzanne said, flipping her brown braid over her shoulder with a toss of her head. "But I guess a week or two is better than nothing."

"Just remember, foster care is supposed to be temporary," reminded Dad. "Yes, we're open to adoption, and we're very happy that Robbie and Connie could permanently join our family. But sometimes we just need to provide a safe place for children to stay for a little while when they can't be with their biological parents."

That evening the coming baby was the main topic of discussion. Mother pulled out a box of baby clothes she kept on hand. Marilyn put a clean sheet on the crib mattress, and Suzanne and Connie found two baby boy blankets. They folded them just so and hung them over the crib railing.

The next day the girls could hardly contain their anticipation. Before picking up the girls after school, Mother went to town to buy disposable diapers and formula. When Twila went into the baby's room to put away the diapers and baby wipes, she could hear Suzanne, Connie, and Rita in the hallway, arguing over who was going to hold the baby first.

"I get to hold him first because I'm the oldest," Suzanne informed her two younger sisters.

"Well, I'm the youngest, so you should let *me* be first," protested Rita.

"But then *I* never get to be first!" wailed Connie. "I'm in the middle, so *this* time I should get to have the first turn!"

Twila hurried past them and went to see what else needed to be done before the new baby arrived.

It was 4:45, and the younger girls were beginning to think they couldn't wait a minute more when Mrs. Gunther's car rolled in the driveway. Mrs. Gunther came in, set Dustin's car seat on the dining room table, and began to unwrap his blankets. But when she unbuckled him and lifted him out, he wasn't the little baby the girls were expecting.

"He's so big!" exclaimed Rita.

Mrs. Gunther chuckled. "He's long for his age. Both his parents are quite tall, so I'm sure that's why." She handed the baby to Mother. Dustin looked up at Mother with startled blue eyes. His face puckered and he started to cry. Mother lifted him to her shoulder and rocked him gently. He soon calmed and the girls gathered around to get a peek at him.

When Mrs. Gunther brought some papers for Mother to sign, Mother handed the baby to Connie. "Remember to watch his back," she cautioned. "Just because he's big doesn't mean he can handle himself like an older baby."

Connie took him to the living room couch where she could cuddle him and get a better look, and the other girls gathered around. Dustin looked around at them with wide eyes and for the moment seemed to enjoy the attention. "Oh, look! He smiled!" said Rita.

While the younger girls exclaimed over Dustin's blue eyes and blond curls, Mrs. Gunther explained to Mother what she knew of Dustin's feeding and sleeping schedule.

Mrs. Gunther gathered all her papers into a neat stack and then paused. "There's one more thing I'd like to discuss with you while I'm here." Twila listened with one ear as her sisters coaxed Dustin to smile again.

"A few weeks ago a little girl came into our care," Mrs. Gunther was saying. "Her name is Tanisha. Her father's dead, and her mother disappeared two years ago. We don't know where she is. Tanisha had been in the care of an elderly aunt, but right now she's staying with another one of our foster families.

"It's very likely we'll be looking for a permanent home for her. We'd like to place her as quickly as possible with a family who would consider adoption. Knowing you're open to adoption, we're presenting her situation to you and your husband. You have experience with adopting older children, so we feel that your family would be a good one for Tanisha."

Mother looked a bit dazed. "How old is this child?"

Mrs. Gunther sifted absently through her stack of papers. "She's four, but I must tell you this child was profoundly neglected. From what we've learned, she received minimal care. She often didn't have enough to eat, and her basic needs were seldom met.

"Tanisha's social skills are surprisingly good. The aunt who cared for her suffered from Alzheimer's and only occasionally remembered to send her to preschool. Apparently preschool is where she picked up what skills she has—along with the fact that she's extremely intelligent."

"How is she doing with the family she's currently with?" asked Mother.

"She's doing fine, but that's not necessarily a good sign," said Mrs. Gunther. "Children who have been neglected or abused tend to go through what we call a 'honeymoon stage' before they begin to display their real behavior."

Twila edged closer to Mother and Mrs. Gunther so she could hear better. This sounded very interesting, but a little scary!

Mrs. Gunther went on, "Because of the trauma Tanisha has experienced, she'll very likely display some challenging behavior.

She seems very independent and resists connecting to any caregiver. If you recall, attachment was one of the issues we touched on briefly in foster parent training. You may face some difficulties in parenting this child, but we believe that with structure and love, Tanisha would be a wonderful addition to a family like yours."

Twila glanced over at Marilyn, who raised her eyebrows. Twila couldn't remember Mrs. Gunther discussing any previous foster child with such gravity. What did she mean by "attachment"? Twila had never heard Mrs. Gunther or her parents mention this term before when describing a child in need of a home.

Thoughtfully, Mrs. Gunther drummed her fingers on the table. "I know this is a big decision, but we'd really like to have an answer by next week. It's of utmost importance to place Tanisha with a family as soon as possible. Permanency is very important for helping children with attachment problems to heal and mature. Talk it over with Mr. Hammond. If you're willing to seriously consider it, let us know and we'll give you further information," Mrs. Gunther finished.

"Well, Alex and I will definitely want to pray about this," Mother answered slowly. "If we're interested, we'll try to let you know soon."

Mrs. Gunther left. The baby was getting fussy, so Mother warmed a bottle for him. She sat down to feed him, and Dustin hungrily drank a couple of ounces. But when he looked up into Mother's face, he gave that same startled cry and refused to eat any more. Mother wrapped him snugly in a blanket and cuddled him close. Eventually, he cried himself to sleep. Mother tucked him gently into his bed and, to the relief of the girls, he stayed sleeping. They were accustomed to the fears new children expressed when they first came, but that didn't make it any easier to listen to their heartbreaking cries.

Twila was nearly bursting to ask Mother about the little girl Mrs. Gunther had mentioned. But she sensed Mother didn't want to discuss it in front of the younger girls, so she waited until Mother had sent Suzanne, Connie, and Rita off on some errands and she and Marilyn were helping Mother make supper before she brought up the subject.

Marilyn was enthusiastic. "Mother, you and Dad wouldn't turn that poor little Tanisha away, would you? I feel so sorry for her. Imagine being raised by an aunt who had Alzheimer's. Great-Aunt Grace has Alzheimer's, and nobody would think of letting her take care of a child!"

Mother was slow to answer. "We must carefully consider everything before we make a decision like this," she said at last. "It hasn't been very long since Connie's and Robbie's adoptions were finalized. They're doing well, but they still have adjustments to go through. They may not be able to handle having an emotionally disturbed child in our home. And what about you girls? Are you sure you could be patient with a challenging child disrupting our home? It will take more than just love. It will take commitment to have a child like Tanisha in our family."

"But, Mother." Twila hesitated. "Even if Tanisha does have problems, wouldn't that mean she needs the love of a family even more?"

"You're right," Mother agreed. "She may not have a lot of needs, but we must be prepared. And yes, the more behavior problems she has, the more love she'll need, and the more we'll need God's help. But are *we* the right family for her? Is this what God wants for *us?* I don't know a lot about attachment problems. Dad and I will talk about it, and in the meantime you girls can pray. Think about it too. You girls are getting old enough that I'm sure Dad will want to hear your input on this."

"I can't help but think about it!" declared Marilyn. "The story of that little girl is haunting."

In the following days, Twila did ponder and pray about the situation. It tugged at her heart to think of a four-year-old girl alone and unwanted in the world. But something within her also resisted the thought of the changes this could bring to their home. She was just as happy as the rest of the family when a new child came into their home, and she loved Robbie and Connie very much. But she also liked the tranquil times when it was just their family. She didn't take to change like some of her other sisters. Or thrive on the happy chaos, like Suzanne had when Wyatt and some of the other children had stayed with them.

Twila liked her family just the way it was. She wasn't sure she was ready for something different—at least, not this big of a change.

The word *attachment* churned in her mind. She wasn't sure she quite understood what it meant. In spite of her misgivings, the picture of a sad little orphan girl just wouldn't go away.

Several evenings later, Dad gathered the family around for devotions. After they sang together, read a chapter of Scripture, and prayed, Dad asked the girls to stay sitting. Twila had noticed that when Dad prayed, he had pled with God for special direction and understanding of His will. Was he planning to tell them of his and Mother's decision about that little girl?

"When Mrs. Gunther brought Dustin a few days ago, she told Mother about a little girl who needs a home," said Dad. "Her name is Tanisha, and she's four years old. If she comes to live with us, it's very likely that we would be able to adopt her. In her home, she had very little care and often didn't have enough to eat. Because of this severe neglect, she may have trouble trusting her new parents or bonding with them. When a child has trouble with this, they call it *reactive attachment disorder,* or *RAD,*" Dad added.

"Mother and I have talked and prayed about it. We've discussed it with several other adoptive parents too. It seems as though God is telling us to go ahead. Tomorrow we plan to meet with Mrs. Gunther, but we wanted to talk with you girls before we made a final decision. So if you girls have any thoughts or objections, we'd like to have you tell us now," Dad finished.

The talk swirled as the family discussed the changes having Tanisha in their home would mean for them.

"If she comes, where will she sleep?" wondered Rita. "Can she sleep with us younger girls?"

"No," said Dad. "If Tanisha comes, she will sleep in the bedroom that we keep for all the children who come into our home for foster care."

"I think we should let her come. I don't care if she does have this attachment problem," said Suzanne decidedly. "I think it would be fun to have another girl in the family."

"Too bad she's not a boy," said Connie. "Then Robbie wouldn't be the only boy in our family."

"Dad's a boy!" said Robbie stoutly. Then he looked puzzled when the family laughed.

Marilyn spoke up next. "Ever since Mother told us older girls about Tanisha, I just can't get her out of my mind. If you and Mother decide she can come, I'd be happy. But RAD does sound serious and scary!"

"We haven't heard from you yet, Twila," Dad said. "What are you thinking?"

Twila ran her hand back and forth over the cushioned arm of the couch. She liked the soft, smooth feel under her hand. At last she said slowly, "I like our family the way it is. There are already six of us children. But it seems kind of selfish to say no just because I think our family is big enough. I guess I'll just be happy with whatever you and Mother decide."

Suzanne brushed some strands of her brown hair back from her face with a restless motion. Twila knew Suzanne didn't like her response. Suzanne had decided opinions about most every-thing, and in this case she was all for having Tanisha come live with them.

But before Suzanne could jump in with her opinion, Rita asked, "What *is* sweeper's disease?"

A look of total bewilderment crossed Dad's face.

Suzanne giggled. "She's thinking of *attachments*, like we use for the vacuum sweeper."

Dad looked at Mother. "Why don't you tell her? You'll be able to explain it better than I can. What is attachment disorder, and why do some children have this trouble?"

"Well," said Mother, "we learned a little about it in foster care classes. When children have been neglected or hurt by those who take care of them, or they are separated from their mothers, they may have a hard time feeling close to anyone, especially their mothers. Those who study child development think that's because children who have been hurt or neglected while in their mother's care can't trust their mother to love them, take care of them, and keep them safe. So they may not bond, or *attach*, to their moth-ers like most babies do. It doesn't feel safe for them to be close to other people. They are lonely, but it feels better to take care of themselves."

Dad nodded and added, "A happy, secure child likes to be close to his mother, but some children are afraid to trust their mothers. When children don't feel safe trusting their parents, it's harder for them to obey any kind of authority, because it feels danger-ous to them."

Robbie ran over to Mother and asked to be held. She pulled him up, and as he snuggled into her arms, Mother said, "Children whose parents hurt them or neglect them may become very fear-ful and angry. Because of their fear and anger, they may push away or ignore others who try to love them and take care of them.

Families who want to bring such children into their homes may find their behavior disruptive and hard to manage. Children who have trouble bonding with their new families don't respond to discipline in the same way as do children who feel safe and loved."

Connie snuggled up to Mother. "I'm sure we won't have any problems. Tanisha won't be able to help but love you. You're the best mother in the whole world!"

Mother slipped an arm around Connie and gave her a squeeze. "Thank you, Connie. I'm glad you think so!"

Dad and Mother exchanged a glance, and then Dad spoke. "Well, it doesn't seem like you girls have any particular objections, and Mother and I feel God is nudging us to move ahead. So tomorrow we'll talk to Mrs. Gunther about the possibility of Tanisha coming to live with us."

The younger girls cheered and Marilyn smiled, but Twila said nothing. Her feelings were so mixed, she didn't know how she felt. Yet in spite of her conflicting emotions, Twila was glad she had parents she could trust to make the best decision for their family.

As planned, Mother and Dad went to see Mrs. Gunther the next day. They left after lunch and were still gone when Grandma Hammond brought the girls home after school. The girls waited anxiously, wondering about the outcome of the visit.

"Why don't we take a walk back through the woods to the Grahams'?" Marilyn suggested. "A lot of the snow has melted so it shouldn't be too hard walking. And I want to take this bird book over to Mrs. Graham."

"I'm not going," objected Suzanne. "There will be nothing to see in the woods this time of year anyway. And it will still be too hard to walk."

"Oh, come on," coaxed Twila. "It won't be that bad!"

Suzanne refused to get dressed until she saw that all the others were getting ready to go out. Then she reluctantly pulled on her boots and coat and joined them.

"I'm going to see if I can find something in the woods to show Mrs. Graham," Rita announced.

"You won't find anything. Everything's dead," Suzanne said scornfully.

Rita looked rather hurt, and Twila wished Suzanne would at least try to be nice. But she understood why Suzanne felt irritable. Twila felt restless too, not knowing for sure if Tanisha would be joining their family.

"I'll help you look for something for Mrs. Graham," said Marilyn, soothing Rita's rumpled feelings.

They were nearing the fence line between their land and the Grahams' when Connie suddenly exclaimed, "Look over there! A deer!"

The girls watched as the deer looked at them curiously and then suddenly turned, leaped over the fence, and ran away.

"Do you think it was a buck or a doe?" wondered Rita.

"Of course it's a doe," said Suzanne peevishly. "It didn't have any antlers."

Ignoring Suzanne's disagreeable mood, Twila explained, "By this time of year, the bucks have shed their antlers, and you can't tell which is which."

"Well, maybe it was a buck then. He was so big!" decided Rita as she stepped along in Marilyn's tracks.

Suzanne stomped on ahead of the other girls and then slowed as she carefully made her way through a big drift. But she still got her boots full of snow. She leaned against a nearby tree and emptied out her boots one at a time. "I told you girls the snow was still too deep."

"Look at those pine cones way up at the top of that tree," said Marilyn, trying to distract Suzanne from her grouching.

"Too bad we couldn't take some of them to Mrs. Graham. She'd know exactly what kind of pine tree it is," said Rita.

Twila tipped her head back to see where the girls were pointing and said, "I wonder how many different species of pine trees there are in Wisconsin? Let's ask Mrs. Graham when we get there."

Mrs. Graham was a naturalist. The Hammonds had gotten to know the Grahams only in the last several years. Since then, Mother and the girls had often gone to Mrs. Graham with questions about plants and trees. Pleased with their interest in the things she loved, Mrs. Graham willingly shared from her wealth of knowledge.

Mr. Graham was a plumber, and he and Dad had gotten acquainted when they had worked together on the same construction job. Because of this, the two families had become friends. Mrs. Graham had lost her leg to due to uncontrolled diabetes, and now Marilyn often helped her an afternoon or two a week.

Soon the girls were knocking at the Grahams' door. Marilyn poked her head inside. "Hello," she called out. "Is anyone home?"

"Of course I'm home! Where else would I be?" came Mrs. Graham's brisk voice. "Come on in before you let all the cold air in."

Accustomed to her abrupt way of speaking, the girls let themselves in. They took off their boots and went into the living room where the handicapped woman was sitting in her wheelchair.

Mrs. Graham's tone softened a little when the girls entered with bright eyes and rosy cheeks. "Well, well, what are you girls up to? No trouble, I hope!"

Marilyn laid the bird book in the older woman's lap and explained. "Mother bought this book at a thrift store, and we thought you'd like to see it." Marilyn was about to go on, but Mrs. Graham was already paging through the book, a gleam of interest in her eyes.

"My, this is fascinating! It has really nice pictures and a lot of details!" exclaimed Mrs. Graham. She paged some more and then, somewhat reluctantly, she laid the volume on the stand beside her and turned to her guests. "Do you mind if I borrow it for a few days?"

"Of course not," said Marilyn. "That's why we brought it."

"While we were walking over here, we were noticing the different kinds of pines," Twila said. "We were wondering if you could tell us how many different species of pine trees there are in Wisconsin."

Mrs. Graham sat forward in her chair. "Are you talking about just evergreens, or do you mean coniferous trees as well?"

The girls looked confused, so Mrs. Graham went on. "Coniferous trees are any kind of tree that makes a cone. That includes both hemlocks and evergreens. An evergreen is any kind of tree that keeps its foliage all year or for several years. Hemlocks differ from other pine trees in their structure. A hemlock has slender branches that tend to droop. The needles are short and flat and blunt-tipped. There are only nine different species of hemlocks in the world."

Mrs. Graham leaned back and took a deep breath. "This is really interesting, girls! I'm glad you brought it up. Now, let me see, what was your question? Oh yes, how many kinds of pine trees do we have in our state? Well, there are almost forty different species in the United States and Canada, but here in Wisconsin we have just six. We have the balsam fir and the jack pine. We also have the Norway pine, which in our area is probably more commonly known as the red pine. Then there's the white pine, the white spruce, and the black spruce, which is also called the Scotch pine."

Mrs. Graham chuckled. "How was that for today's science lesson? I could tell you a lot more, but I don't want to bore you. When I get started talking about plants and trees, I don't know when to stop. But anytime you have questions, I'll try to answer as well as I can."

"Oh, no, it's not a bit boring," Twila assured her. "But we really do need to go. Mother and Dad went to see Mrs. Gunther about a new little girl, and we want to be home when they get back."

The crispness crept back into Mrs. Graham's voice. "So you're going to take in another child? You already have six! Don't you think you have enough children in your family?"

Suzanne's eyes flashed with resentment at Mrs. Graham's tone. "Of course not!" she said a bit shortly. "If a child needs a home, we're glad to give her one. Wouldn't you want someone to give you a home if you didn't have a mother or father?"

A faraway look came into Mrs. Graham's eyes. "I suppose I would. But it doesn't seem to be the popular thing nowadays to be concerned about orphans. Oh, people may pretend to be. They'll dish out money now and then, but not many want to put themselves out for some little terror that messes up their family! But your family is different. You don't just talk; you take action. I suppose I respect you more than I want to admit."

Feeling vaguely unsettled and not sure what Mrs. Graham meant, Twila joined her sisters in putting on their boots to walk home again. By the time they arrived, Dad, Mother, Robbie, and baby Dustin had just gotten home.

The girls were bursting with curiosity, and the younger girls eagerly plied Dad and Mother with questions.

"Did you talk to Mrs. Gunther?" asked Rita even before she had taken off her coat.

"What did she say?" asked Connie.

Suzanne gave her boots a kick in the general direction of where they belonged and asked, "Is Tanisha coming to live with us?"

Dad set two grocery bags on the kitchen table and teased, "If you would stop talking all at once, maybe we could answer your questions."

Twila bent over to pull Dustin out of his car seat. Something stirred uneasily within her. She wasn't sure she wanted to hear what Dad had to say. She laid Dustin on the table, took off his snowsuit, and cuddled him. His blond curls felt soft against her cheek.

Dad was talking. "We discussed it with Mrs. Gunther, and we told her that we'd like Tanisha to come live with us."

The younger girls cheered. Twila kissed the top of Dustin's head. She couldn't decide if she wanted to rejoice with the other girls or groan. Mrs. Graham's words replayed in her mind. *Not many people want to put themselves out for some little terror that messes up their family.* Twila wondered if she was being selfish and uncaring like "most people" as Mrs. Graham had said. Would Tanisha mess up their home? She remembered Mrs. Graham's praise of the Hammond family. Twila flushed, thinking, *What would Mrs. Graham think of me if she knew how reluctant I feel to have Tanisha come live with us?*

But the excitement of the younger girls was catching. Suddenly Twila felt relieved. At least now that she knew Tanisha was coming, she no longer had to wonder and feel as if she were hanging in the balance.

Maybe it won't be as bad as I think. God has always been with us in the past. Surely He will not desert us now. Twila comforted herself with that thought.

What *would* this new little girl be like? They would soon find out.

Tanisha

Excitement rippled through the house. It had been less than two weeks since the Hammonds had heard about Tanisha, and now today was the day she was coming!

What would Tanisha be like? Would she be shy? How tall would she be? What color was her hair? Did she talk much? What foods did she like? The younger girls had asked all these questions and many more. Now they would soon get some answers.

It was Saturday, and the girls and Mother had cleaned the house in record time. The dishes were done, and the windows and floors were shining and spotless.

Tanisha's room had been cleaned at least three times by eager sisters anxious to do something to welcome this new little stranger into their home. They had changed the comforter on the bed to a pink and yellow one. The three middle sisters were sure the blue one Wyatt had used would never do for a girl.

The curtains were getting old and faded, so Mother had bought some pink and purple fabric that Marilyn and Twila were sure would please the heart of any little girl. Mother hadn't had time to sew the new curtains. She told the disappointed younger girls that a loving welcome would mean more to Tanisha than new curtains.

Rita found one of her dolls in the toy box. "I'm going to put this dolly on Tanisha's bed," she told her sisters.

Robbie watched her lay the doll against the pillow on Tanisha's bed and exclaimed, "I wanna do som-ping for 'Nisha too!"

So Rita, ever the peacemaker, quickly found a piece of candy from her hidden stash in a drawer. "Here, Robbie! You can give her this." Robbie clutched the peppermint tightly in his hand, a satisfied smile creeping over his face, and Twila was sure it would be sticky and spoiled until he was able to give it to Tanisha.

Dustin had gone back to his parents, but the excitement of Tanisha's coming helped the girls not to miss him quite so much.

Dad had planned to be home when Tanisha arrived, but then Grandma called to say she had a water leak. Uncle Jerry and Aunt Julia were away, so Dad went to Grandma Hammond's to fix it. Mother and the girls waited alone.

The longer they waited, the more restless Robbie became. "Why don't you bring me a book?" Mother suggested. Robbie ran to get his favorite bear book.

They had gotten halfway through the story when a shout rose from Rita, who had posted herself at the living room window. "Mrs. Gunther is here!"

The bear book was quickly abandoned, and Mother went to the door to welcome the new arrivals.

All eyes were drawn to the slight figure holding on to Mrs. Gunther's hand. As she stepped through the door, Mrs. Gunther set down two small grocery bags of Tanisha's things and reached out to help the little girl unzip her coat. But Tanisha turned away from the social worker and did it herself. She let her coat fall to the floor and then proceeded to kick off a pair of little boy's blue boots.

Mrs. Gunther picked up Tanisha's faded pink coat and handed it to Tanisha. "Ask Mrs. Hammond where she would like you to put your coat and boots," she instructed.

Tanisha turned to Mother. "Where do you want me to put my coat and boots?" she said mechanically.

Mother showed her the hook where she could hang her coat. The little blue boots were placed neatly against the wall below her coat.

Twila leaned over and whispered to Marilyn, "I have never seen such a beautiful child in all my life!" Tanisha was petite for her age. Her African and Caucasian heritage blended together in her creamy brown skin. Her eyes were dark and her features delicate. But it was her hair that caught the attention of all the Hammond sisters. It was dark brown and very thick. Tanisha's other foster mom had parted and combed it into cornrows. The many braids hung down past the child's shoulders.

When Tanisha's coat was hung up, she suddenly spied a potato chip under the cupboard that had somehow passed the notice of the industrious housecleaners of the morning. She darted across the room and picked it up. Before Mrs. Gunther could stop her, she popped it into her mouth and ate it.

Mrs. Gunther smiled wryly. "Well, I guess it won't hurt her."

The first glimpse of Tanisha had told the girls what she looked like, and before long they knew the answer to another question as well. Tanisha was *not* shy!

Mrs. Gunther took Tanisha's hand and did the introductions. "This is Tanisha," she told Mother and the girls. "And, Tanisha, this is Mrs. Hammond. Remember I told you that you would be staying with the Hammond family? Let's see if I can tell you all the girls' names." She went around the circle and told Tanisha each one of the girls' and Robbie's names. She got them all right except for Marilyn. She got mixed up and called her Miranda. Friendly laughter helped relieve the nervousness of the moment.

Tanisha hugged Mother and the girls one by one, warming up to them like a long-lost family. She smiled sweetly and looked up at them through long lashes. "I'm so glad I could come to stay at your house!" she told them.

Thrilling with the warmth of her comment and feeling those little arms around her neck, Twila hugged the small child back. She was immediately sure that all her fears had been for nothing.

While Mother and Mrs. Gunther talked, Robbie gave Tanisha the piece of candy. Tanisha took it, and it disappeared almost as rapidly as the chip had. Then Suzanne led her to the toy box and showed her the toys. But Tanisha seemed more interested in talking than in playing. While she talked, she flitted about the room like an exotic butterfly, touching chairs, lamps, books, and toys. "You have such nice toys! May I please look at this book? Why do you have a blue couch? Can I sit on it?" Tanisha asked. But she never really settled down to anything.

The girls were fascinated by the little girl's manners and her ability to hold a conversation. She had a sweetness and charm that promptly captivated their hearts. Marilyn caught Twila's eye and whispered, "Isn't she darling?" Twila nodded back. Tanisha was just the dearest little girl!

Mrs. Gunther was talking to Mother. "I don't suppose you know much about African-American hair care."

"I guess I really know nothing. I've never had any experience," Mother admitted.

Mrs. Gunther opened the smaller of the two bags. "Here are some skin and hair products that her other foster mom used. She said this cocoa butter lotion is the best she's found for Tanisha's skin. As for Tanisha's hair, you likely wouldn't have to braid it in cornrows."

She glanced over at the younger girls. "You could probably comb it much like you do your other girls. Since she's not full African-American, her hair is longer than most and not so kinky. But you may discover that her hair stays healthier when you comb it in lots of braids. If you look in the papers I gave you, you'll find some resources that teach how to care for her type of hair. Tanisha's other foster mom said she'd be happy to teach you anything she knows. I think you'll find it's not as hard as it looks. It's just a matter of learning how to do it."

When Mrs. Gunther and Mother were done talking, Mrs. Gunther turned to leave. "Tanisha," she called.

Tanisha glanced toward Mrs. Gunther and paused in her talk with the little children. Mrs. Gunther said, "I'm leaving now. Goodbye!"

"Goodbye," Tanisha returned casually. "What I was saying, Connie, at my friend's house they have three cats and a dog. The cats were all orange. That lady really liked orange cats, don't you think?" Tanisha continued her stream of chatter as if she didn't notice that Mrs. Gunther, her only connection between this new life and the home she had known before, had just walked out the door.

When Dad came home, Tanisha was not at all afraid of him. She sat down beside him on the couch and asked, "Are you my new daddy?" Twila watched Dad and Tanisha visit freely with each other. *Tanisha is so sweet and eager to please,* she thought.

Tanisha scooted closer to Dad. "I know a song about workin' on the railroad. Wanna hear me sing it?"

"Sure," said Dad kindly. "I'd like to hear you."

Tanisha stood up and in a clear, sweet soprano started singing, "I've been working on the railroad all the live long day. I've been working on the railroad just to pass the time away..."[1]

Tanisha sang the whole song through with wonderful expression. She never missed a single word, and as the song ended, she clipped it short with a flourish. It was so cute that the Hammond sisters all laughed and spontaneously clapped for Tanisha.

---

1 Traditional.

"You did a good job," said Dad with a nod of approval. "Now I want to sing *you* a song. It's called 'Jesus Loves Me.' Do you know that song?" he wondered.

When Tanisha shook her head, Dad asked, "Have you ever heard of Jesus?" Tanisha shook her head again, so Dad went on, "Jesus is the One who made us, and He cares about us very much. I'll sing you the song about Him."

Dad started singing, and some of the other girls joined in. They sang it through once and then again. The second time, Tanisha sang along, and only once did she stumble on the words. Twila marveled how after only one time of hearing it, Tanisha knew the tune perfectly. *What would it be like*, Twila wondered, *to be four years old and never have heard about Jesus?* It would be a privilege to teach Tanisha about Jesus, who loved her.

Later that afternoon, Mother made pizza for supper, and Rita and Tanisha watched as she slid the pan into the oven. When Mother went to the sink and got a dishcloth to clean up her flour mess, Tanisha stood beside her and smiled sweetly up at her. "Mother, may I please help you do something?" she asked.

"Well," said Mother, "you could help Rita set the table. Rita, show Tanisha where we keep the plates, cups, and silverware."

Together the two little girls set the table. After Rita showed her how, Tanisha carefully set each knife, spoon, and fork in perfect order by each plate.

When the pizza was done, the Hammond family gathered around the table and sat down. Dad explained to Tanisha, "Before we eat, we bow our heads and thank God for our food. God is the One who gives us food, a warm house to live in, and many other things. We want to say thank-you to God for being so good to us."

Mother took Tanisha's hands in hers and showed her how to fold her hands. "We must shut our eyes while Dad prays," she said.

For the first time, Twila thought she saw a flicker of resistance in Tanisha's face. But the little girl meekly did as she was told.

When supper was over, Dad told the younger children, "I want you to stack your cup, spoon, fork, and knife on your plate and carry them to the kitchen. Put them on the counter beside the sink. Then you may go play."

Twila knew that Dad was explaining with more detail than he usually did for Tanisha's benefit. The other children already knew what was expected of them once supper was over.

"Okay, Dad," said Tanisha. She laid her silverware and cup on her plate as he had told her and carried them out to the kitchen. When they were finished, Connie, Rita, Tanisha, and Robbie ran off to play, but Suzanne stayed to help Twila with the dishes.

Twila squirted dish soap into the running water and swirled her dishcloth to work up the suds. Suzanne pulled a clean dish towel out of the drawer and exclaimed, "Isn't Tanisha just the sweetest little thing?"

"She's adorable!" Twila agreed. "But I suppose sooner or later we'll see her naughty side too. Surely she won't always be this good."

"I have a hard time believing she'll ever be bad. I think it's so nice that she already calls our parents Mother and Dad just like we do. She's just so darling!" Suzanne said. "I like her name too, even if it does sound a little different."

"Mother says it's an African-American name," Twila explained. "I guess every nationality has a different style of names they like. Robbie's and Connie's Spanish names, Roberto and Consuela, are also a little different than we're used to. But I like their names too."

Suzannne dried a handful of spoons and threw them into the silverware drawer. "I noticed today that her name is spelled T-a-n-i-s-h-a, but we say it Ta-*nee*-sha."

Twila placed another dish in the rack. "Mother said that Tanisha's birth mom's name was Latoya. And I heard Mrs. Gunther call the aunt that took care of her, Rasheeda. I think they have such interesting names!"

Suzanne dried all the plates and put them in one big stack before placing them in the cupboard. She took a serving bowl from the rack and dried it slowly. "You know," she said suddenly, "it's kind of strange though. Most of the children who come are sad or at least a little afraid at first. I wonder why Tanisha doesn't act one bit scared?" She thoughtfully continued to wipe the towel around the already dry bowl. "Maybe it's because she's so glad to be in a real family."

Twila felt a twinge of uneasiness. Suzanne was right. Tanisha's behavior wasn't exactly typical—not compared to the other children who had come to their home. "All children are unique. Maybe Tanisha's just different from the others," Twila told Suzanne, trying to soothe her own misgivings.

The days passed and things continued to go smoothly. The girls went to school during the day, and Robbie and Tanisha stayed home with Mother.

Mother said, "Robbie's becoming spoiled! Tanisha gives him everything he wants and lets him have his own way."

One evening Mother unbraided all of Tanisha's many braids and gave her a bath. She had lotioned Tanisha's skin and gotten her ready for bed when Dad asked for some help in the office.

Mother led Tanisha out to the dining room and laid some hair supplies on the table. "Here, Marilyn," she said. "I'd like you to comb Tanisha's hair. Dad wants me to help him with some book-work so I can't do it right now. We don't dare let it dry without combing it, or we'll have a hard time getting the tangles out."

Marilyn look doubtful. "You're not expecting me to comb it in all those braids, are you?"

"I think it would work to part it down the middle and comb it in two braids. Her hair is not as kinky as some, so you should be able to comb it that way. Put a hair band at the top on each side to hold the hair tight before you braid it," she suggested. "Hopefully sometime I can learn to comb her hair in cornrows, but for tonight we'll do it this way."

Mother left the room, and Marilyn began the task of combing out Tanisha's long wavy hair. She tried to be careful, but she still pulled sometimes. Tanisha sat perfectly still and didn't seem to notice when Marilyn gave an extra hard jerk as she struggled to untangle the curls. "Doesn't it hurt?" Marilyn exclaimed once, when she had accidently pulled harder than she meant to.

The little girl shrugged. "No."

"Wow! You're a brave little girl!" Marilyn complimented.

Ten minutes later, Marilyn stood back and looked at the hair-combing job with satisfaction. "There now, you're all done!" She gave Tanisha a quick hug. "Want to go read a book?"

Robbie heard the word *book*. He gave a cheer and ran to the bookcase. He came back to Marilyn with a huge stack. Robbie, Rita, and Connie piled onto the couch with Marilyn to listen to the story. Tanisha silently sat down with the rest of the children.

Half an hour later, Dad led them all in family devotions, and then Mother went to tuck Robbie and Tanisha into their beds. The girls lingered awhile longer, talking with Dad.

When Mother returned, Twila looked up. "Do you think Robbie will sleep all night? Didn't I hear him crying twice last night?"

Mother nodded. "It was at least twice. He was pretty restless."

"Isn't he kind of big to be still waking up at night?" asked Marilyn. "He's three years old, after all!"

"Yes, he is plenty old," Mother agreed. "The rest of you were easily sleeping through the night at his age. He seems to have a lot of fears, and I want to be there to comfort him as much as possible. I think it may be worse right now because he's adjusting to having Tanisha come."

"What's he afraid of?" wondered Suzanne.

"It doesn't seem that he has many specific fears. It's just fear in general, though sometimes he does talk about being afraid of bears. Often when children are abandoned or have a change of parents, even as little babies, it causes them to be more fearful," Mother explained.

"But don't you get tired of getting up at night?" Rita wondered. "I would be very sleepy the next day if I had to get up that often."

Mother smiled. "I'm glad to! Remember, I didn't get to take care of Robbie for the first fifteen months of his life. I don't mind getting up at night and catching up on some of the rocking that I missed in those months. He's hardly a baby anymore. The day will come soon enough that he won't let me rock him."

"Well, it's time you girls were in bed," Dad remarked. "You have school tomorrow."

Connie gave Dad a hug and then asked Mother as she always did, "You'll come and tuck me in, won't you?"

"Yes," Mother assured her. "I'll come after a bit and tuck you in."

Suzanne—and most of the time, Rita—considered themselves to have outgrown bedtime hugs and kisses. But Connie still clung to nighttime rituals. Twila knew without asking that Mother would say she was happy to still tuck Connie into bed. After all, she hadn't been able to do that in the first eight years of Connie's life.

After school the next day, Marilyn came breezing into the house. "Who wants to go back to the woods with me? Since Mrs. Graham told us how many different pines there are in

Wisconsin, I've been wanting to go and see how many we have in our woods."

Twila was busy with her drawing of Dad. "I'd rather keep working here," she told Marilyn. "Maybe Connie or Suzanne will go with you."

"I'm helping Mother make cookies," said Connie, with an air of importance.

Suzanne shrugged. "It's my turn to do chicken chores, so I guess you'll have to ask Rita if she wants to go with you."

Rita entered the room just then. "What are you going to ask me?" she wondered.

Marilyn replied, "I just wanted to know if any of you girls would like to go back to the woods with me and see how many different kinds of pines we have in our woods. Are you coming with?"

"Sure!" Rita exclaimed. She grabbed her coat, and the two girls were soon out the door.

Twila studied her picture of Dad. She had given it the last finishing touches. She had taken Grandma's advice and adjusted the lines on the walls and ceiling. She still wasn't quite satisfied, but decided it was the best she could do.

Suzanne came into the house with a basket of eggs and set them by the sink to be washed. Seeing Twila scrutinizing her picture, she came and looked over her shoulder.

"That's actually pretty good," Suzanne praised. "Your drawing is getting better all the time. I think you ought to frame it."

"Thank you!" Twila replied. Suzanne didn't often hand out compliments. She seemed to think it her job to see that none of her sisters struggled with pride. "Maybe I will. I'll see if Mother has any frames the right size."

"Twila," Mother called from the kitchen. "Could you watch this spaghetti and set the table? I want to go out to the greenhouse yet before supper and plant some geraniums and impatiens." She took some flower packets off the table. "Please don't forget!" she called over her shoulder as she went out the door.

Twila flushed slighty and scooped up her papers and pencils to put them away. She knew why Mother had added that reminder. Only yesterday she had forgotten to take a sheet of cookies out of the oven. She hadn't remembered them until they were charred black and a burnt odor was wafting through the house. And last week she'd been daydreaming and had added chili powder to the pudding instead of the soup that were both cooking on the stove. Twila knew she needed to do better about her absentmindedness, and she determined they would not be eating burnt spaghetti for supper.

Before she could put away her drawing things, Robbie and Tanisha entered the room together. "Can I see your picture?" Robbie asked.

Twila held the picture down to let him see. Robbie's eyes lit up. "It's Dad! I like it!"

Tanisha looked at the picture too, but made no comment. Thinking she didn't understand, Suzanne said enthusiastically, "Look, Tanisha, it's a picture of Dad. Isn't it nice?" But Tanisha only looked at Suzanne without expression.

"Give her time," said Twila. "After a while she'll think Dad is as wonderful as we do." She tucked her picture in a drawer and went to stir the spaghetti as Mother had asked.

CHAPTER FOUR

Thankful for Snow?

For the most part, Tanisha seemed to adjust easily to the Hammond family. She tripped off happily with the other four- and five-year-olds to Sunday school. She obediently did whatever Dad and Mother asked her to do. She was so eager to please that sometimes Twila thought she was *too* good. Many of the Hammonds' church family and relatives commented on how well she was doing. Twila wondered why Mother never said much.

The month of February had been cold and stormy, but March came in warm and balmy, with very little snow. The ice had scarcely melted off the driveway when one Saturday afternoon the younger girls pulled out their bikes and began pedaling up and down the lane. Robbie got out his trike and rode back and forth on the front sidewalk.

Dad found a tricycle for Tanisha that Rita had used when she was little. Tanisha didn't like to be outdone by Robbie. If he could do something, then she wanted to do it too! But at first she didn't have any idea how to ride a tricycle.

"Here," Dad said, "let me show you how to put your feet on the pedals. You push with your feet like this." With determination, Tanisha put her feet on the pedals, and soon she was zooming up and down the sidewalk with Robbie.

Twila straightened from where she was vacuuming out the van. She looked out the open garage door to where Robbie and Tanisha were riding. She marveled at how well Tanisha was doing.

Though she was determined to keep up with the same speed Robbie was going, or a little faster, never once did her tires slip over the edge of the concrete.

Tanisha hadn't known how to do a lot of things when she had first come. In those early days, she hadn't even known how to use a spoon and fork properly. Apparently she had never used them in her previous homes. But she had mastered each new skill with fierce determination.

Suzanne called from the driveway, "Twila, look what I can do!" She lifted her hands off the handlebars and rode several yards. Then she hit a dip in the lane, and the front of her bike started to wobble. Grinning, Suzanne grabbed the bars and kept going.

Connie, who was riding close behind Suzanne, hit the same dip. She had been watching Suzanne and wasn't paying attention. She hit the hole wrong and went sprawling.

"Are you hurt, Connie?" Twila called.

Connie jumped up. "I'm fine!" she called back. "But my belt is caught in the chain." She jerked and tugged, but the sash of her dress was firmly entwined in the chain and teeth of the sprocket. Wordlessly, she kept yanking on it, trying to free herself.

Just then Mother came out to the garage to put some loaves of fresh bread in the freezer and check on the children. She noticed Connie struggling to get loose and walked out to help her. At Mother's request, Twila turned off the vacuum cleaner and went along.

Together she and Mother turned the pedal until the belt was free. After all Connie's yanking, her dress was torn and greasy.

Mother looked at the ruined sash. "You'd better go in and change your dress before it gets wrecked any worse," she told Connie. "And next time, when you have a problem, do you think maybe you could ask for help instead of trying to do it yourself? If you would have called for someone, your dress wouldn't have gotten so much grease on it, and it wouldn't have torn so badly."

Connie looked at Mother in surprise. "Sure, I can ask for help! I didn't know you wanted me to."

Mother smiled and put an arm around Connie. "Oh yes! It's a good idea to ask for help when there's something you can't do. Mothers like to help their children when something is too hard for them."

Connie followed Mother into the house, and Twila went back to cleaning out the van. Robbie rode his tricycle up to the van and sat watching her, his arms propped on the trike handles. Twila vacuumed for a while and then noticed a book under one of the seats. She held it out to Robbie. "Do you want to take this book to the house and put it in the bookcase?"

"No thank you!" said Robbie airily. Grabbing the handlebars, he quickly pedaled away. Half amused and half disgusted, Twila took the book into the house herself.

By the time Twila had finished cleaning the van, Robbie had long since wandered off to do something else, but Tanisha was still riding her trike up and down the sidewalk. Her face held no look of pleasure, but she seemed to be getting some measure of satisfaction out of doing the same thing over and over again.

Tanisha spoke up suddenly. "The neighbors have a gray cat in their window."

Twila was surprised. She looked across the road to the Bensons' house. Shading her eyes, she squinted to get a better look at the neighbors' living room window. Sure enough, she could faintly see a cat draped over the back of a chair. And it did look like the cat was gray!

"Wow, you have good eyes!" Twila commented. But Tanisha pedaled past her as if she didn't hear.

Twila was lugging the vacuum sweeper back into the house when Robbie burst through the door shouting, "Mama, Mama! Look what Rita and I found! A Daniel-lion!"

"Well, sure enough you *did* find a dandelion!" exclaimed Mother. "Already! Where did you find it?"

Rita had followed Robbie in. "It was right up against the house in the back where the sun shines," she said.

Marilyn was in the kitchen washing some baking dishes. She helped Rita and Robbie find a small vase in the cupboard. The younger children put the single blossom in the vase and placed it on the dining room table.

The screen door banged and Tanisha came in. She silently took in Rita's and Robbie's enthusiasm over the first dandelion of spring. Rita held up the flower for her to see. "Look, isn't it pretty?"

"No!" said Tanisha. "It's ugly." Seemingly oblivious to the fact that her nasty comment had thrown cold water on Rita's and Robbie's happiness, she drifted aimlessly through the living room. She flitted over to the window and stood there for a long time.

Twila wondered what she was thinking. Why didn't Tanisha connect with the simple joys that delighted her younger siblings? Was Tanisha happy here? She didn't act afraid of them, but neither did she seem glad to be in their home. Did she miss her mother or her aunt or her previous foster family? Why did she never talk about them? Never once had Twila heard Tanisha mention anything that had happened to her before she had joined the Hammond family. It suddenly struck Twila that even after all these weeks, they still knew very little about Tanisha. She had an amazing ability to say a lot of words without saying anything of importance.

Tanisha turned away from the window and went back outside. Her eyes had a blank look, as if she wasn't paying attention to anything around her. But Twila had the feeling Tanisha was taking in much more than she let on. How had she noticed an obscure detail like the cat in the neighbors' window? A casual observer would have never picked that up.

Marilyn's eyes also followed the small girl as she went out. She crossed to the window to see where she had gone. "Tanisha's out there riding her tricycle again," she said. She stood quietly for a few moments, watching; then she turned to Twila. "There's something strange about that child. Do you think she's happy here? She never says one way or the other."

"Don't you remember? She said she was glad to be at our house when she first came," said Twila.

"Oh, yes! I remember that," replied Marilyn. "But she hasn't said much about it since then." She looked out the window again. "Have you noticed how she never asks for anything? Not even a drink of water. If she wants one, she just climbs up on the counter and gets it. And she never goes to Mother like Robbie does for his bumps and bruises. I've seen her fall down, and it has to hurt! But she just jumps up as if she doesn't even feel it."

Twila was startled. So Marilyn was noticing too!

Twila felt a sudden uneasiness. She tried to push the feeling away. "She used to ask for help sometimes right at first, but she doesn't anymore," Twila told Marilyn. "I did hear her ask someone at church for a tissue last Sunday. But she could have easily gotten it herself. Though I don't know why she wanted a tissue at church when she refuses to use them at home. But don't you think we need to give her more time?" Twila asked hopefully. "I'm sure she's still adjusting."

"I hope you're right. She's probably still settling in," Marilyn replied. "But there's something about her that puzzles me. I can't quite explain it. She's sweet and good . . . but it's almost like she's *too* good. Somehow I get the feeling that she's always pretending . . . like we're not seeing the real Tanisha. Do you know what I mean?"

"I know exactly what you mean! But it would be very hard to explain it to anyone. One thing—that I guess is to be expected—is that she swears."

"Does she ever!" Marilyn agreed. "She's got quite the vocabulary! But even though it's not right, at least that seems more normal than some of her other behavior. I'm sure no one ever told her not to say those words before she was put in foster care. So how was she supposed to know that swearing is wrong?"

Twila nodded. "Well, one thing you can say for sure. She's as cute as a button! I've never seen a child with such a pretty little face. But . . . " Twila paused. "Looks aren't everything!"

Marilyn turned to look back out the window at the little figure still riding up and down the sidewalk. "Beauty sure won't be what gets her through life," she agreed.

The girls turned as Mother came in carrying something. She walked across the room and set it on the table.

"Our dollhouse!" Marilyn and Twila exclaimed together.

"Where did you find it?" Marilyn wondered. "I haven't seen that little house in years."

"It's been up in the attic," Mother replied. "I thought it might be something Tanisha would enjoy playing with. Except for riding her tricycle, she just kind of drifts around and never sticks to anything. Maybe this will catch her interest."

Marilyn and Twila crowded close, examining the tiny chairs, tables, and beds. Twila held up two of the dolls. "Remember how this red-haired doll was always my favorite? You always liked this other one with the blue dress best, so we got along well."

Marilyn took the doll and smoothed its blonde hair. "That's right, this was my favorite doll. I almost forgot we even had this dollhouse."

"Well, I was wondering if you girls could clean it up," Mother said. "Rita and Suzanne never played with it like you older girls did. So for the last several years, it's just sat up in the attic collecting dust."

The girls went to get a bucket of soapy water and some rags and started scrubbing. The pieces were small, and it was tedious work. But they hardly noticed as they reminisced about the fun they used to have and the spats they had gotten into over the dollhouse.

After they finished cleaning the dollhouse accessories, they cleaned the little house itself. They set the new toy in a corner of the living room, and Twila went to empty the water pail while Marilyn went to find Tanisha. They were eager to see what she would think of the dollhouse.

Tanisha came in, trailing behind Marilyn, her face blank.

"Look, Tanisha!" said Twila. "Look what Mother found in the attic!" Tanisha looked but made no comment. Her face was void of expression.

"We used to play with it when we were little like you," Marilyn added. "Don't you think it will be fun to play with?"

Still Tanisha had nothing to say. She continued to stare blankly. Then she stepped closer and began to handle the pieces, her quick fingers moving from object to object. Twila thought she saw a brief spark of interest flash over Tanisha's face. But just as quickly, the look was gone, and her empty expression returned.

Her eyes look almost haunted, Twila thought. Her eyes met Marilyn's look of disappointment. She had hoped Tanisha would show at least some delight in the dollhouse. She did seem to want to play with it, so the girls left her to play with it undisturbed.

When Twila walked by the dollhouse later, she noticed that Tanisha had carefully arranged the doll furniture according to rooms. But most of the dolls were lying on the floor of the dollhouse. Only one dark-haired little girl doll stood up straight and tall among them. "Who is that doll?" Twila asked curiously.

"It's me," said Tanisha without hesitation. "See, her hair is the same color as mine."

Twila smiled to herself. It was what she had thought. Maybe Tanisha was more pleased with the dollhouse than she had first let on. It was interesting to see Tanisha's creativity. Twila remembered how imaginative she and Marilyn had been when they played with those dolls.

The next Monday when the girls got into the van after school, the first thing Robbie said was, "We're going to Grandma's tonight." The younger girls cheered while Marilyn and Twila looked to Mother for an explanation.

"Dad and Uncle Jerry have some money matters they want to discuss with Grandma," Mother explained. "Dad wants to go over to Grandma's as soon as supper is over."

As they rode home, the other girls chattered with Mother. Twila noticed that as early as it was, it was already getting dark. It had been cloudy all day. "I wonder if we're going to get a storm?" she asked.

"When we came out of the schoolhouse, I noticed the temperature had dropped since last recess. I'm guessing we're in for some snow," Marilyn said.

"Not more snow!" objected Rita. "We haven't had snow for weeks, and it's been so warm."

"It wouldn't be unusual for around here if we did get snow," Mother remarked. "Our spring came early this year, and we're bound to have some more cold weather yet."

When they got home, Tanisha seemed restless. A little later, Twila noticed that she was hiding around the corner of the couch, curled up in a ball and rocking herself back and forth.

When Mother found Tanisha there, she picked her up and carried her to the rocking chair. She sang as she rocked Tanisha for a long time. But the stiff little figure never relaxed. When Mother had to get up to finish supper, she took Tanisha out to the kitchen and sat her on a chair nearby while she worked. Tanisha curled her feet underneath her. She pulled the hood of her sweater over her head and face as far as it would go.

The younger girls looking questioningly at Mother, but Mother only shook her head and put a finger to her lips. Whatever was bothering Tanisha, Mother didn't seem to know either. So the girls went about their work and tried not to pay attention to the huddled little figure. Meanwhile, outside, it started to snow in huge fluffy flakes.

"Dad's home!" Robbie squealed. He ran to the entryway and waited for Dad to come in. Moments later Dad walked into the kitchen with Robbie laughing on his shoulders.

Mother was dishing up the food. She looked up from where she was standing at the stove and smiled. "We're just about ready to eat," she said.

Dad glanced at the little figure in the chair and then at Mother. Mother returned his questioning look with a slight raise of her eyebrows.

Dad swung Robbie down and set him on his feet. He reached into his pocket and set a roll of stamps on the table. "Here are these stamps you said you needed," he told Mother.

"Thank you," Mother replied. "The girls used the last ones we had for some letters today." She looked at Rita. "Why don't you go put them on Dad's desk?"

Dad went to wash up, and the rest of the family gathered to eat. At Mother's prompting, Tanisha slipped quietly out of her chair and slid into her spot at the table. Whatever had been bothering her didn't seem to prevent her from eating.

During supper Dad kept glancing out the window. It was snowing harder all the time, and Twila knew he was debating whether or not they should go to Grandma's. "I guess we'll go," he decided. "I think we'll be fine if we take it slowly."

The girls and Mother quickly cleaned up the kitchen and got ready to go. As they got in the van and pulled out onto the road, the snow was coming down with blinding force. It was so hard to see that Twila was afraid Dad would turn around and go home. After anticipating for several hours that they were going to Grandma's, she didn't want to have to spend the evening at home.

Dad drove a little farther, peering through the storm. At last he put his foot to the brakes. "It's too hard to see the road. We'll just have to turn around and go back. It's not safe to keep going like this!"

Twila was disappointed. Suzanne evidently felt the same, for she sputtered, "Of all the disgusting things! It's already April, and we've been having such nice weather. We even had dandelions! Now we're getting all this snow, and we can't even go to Grandma Hammond's. Who wants more snow anyway? I'm tired of it!"

"Well, would you rather keep going and end up in the ditch?" Marilyn asked.

"That would be more exciting than just going home!" Suzanne said contrarily.

Back home, the evening passed quietly. Suzanne found a book and flopped on the couch. Twila got her own book and sat down to read. Connie pled with Marilyn to help her study for an English test. So they sat at the dining room table, and Marilyn drilled her on nouns, verbs, adverbs, and adjectives.

Dad stepped into the living room and noticed the small figure of Tanisha huddled in a chair. He scooped her up and carried her to the rocker. He whistled a low tune as he rocked back and forth. Suddenly Twila picked up the melody, and she looked up sharply. Was Dad thinking about the song he was whistling?

"The children are the broken pieces.

When a home falls apart, the children are the broken pieces.

Who's gonna mend their tender hearts?"[2]

Twila contemplated the little girl in Dad's arms. She thought of the other children who had come through their home. She thought of the broken little hearts. Suddenly the calling of helping hurting children seemed high and noble. She was glad God had led Dad and Mother to reach out to children in this way. Twila determined she would do all she could to help her parents love Tanisha back to health and happiness.

Dad kept on rocking, but Tanisha just sat there with her eyes closed. Dad whistled the last words of the song: "God, come and mend the broken pieces."[3]

Please, Lord, whatever broken pieces there may be in Tanisha's heart, come and mend them, Twila prayed inwardly before turning back to her book.

Mother sat in a nearby chair, embroidering. Robbie was playing with farm toys. Rita helped him set up his fences for a pasture for his cows. They hunted in the toy box for farm animals and placed them in the proper places about the farm.

Robbie decided it was time to work in his fields. He hitched the plow to his tractor and, making engine noises, drove out to the field. After driving back and forth for a while, he announced, "Now I'm going to bale hay." He went to look for his baler on the shelf where he normally kept his toy tractors and implements, but it wasn't there. He couldn't find it in the toy box either.

---

2 Copyright © 1982 Dawn Treader Music (SESAC) Shepherd's Fold Music (BMI) (adm. at CapitolCMGPublishing.com) All rights reserved. Used by permission.
3 Ibid.

"Rita!" he exclaimed. "Where's my baler? Can't find it." Together the two of them looked for the baler, but it was nowhere to be found.

Suddenly Tanisha slid off Dad's lap. She went to the back of the couch and pulled out the baler. Rita exclaimed, "How did you know it was back there?" Tanisha shrugged.

"You can play with us," Robbie offered generously. He handed Tanisha a tractor, but she just sat on the floor with the tractor in her lap, watching.

Robbie looked puzzled. "Don't you know how to play tractors?" he asked. Tanisha only stared back at him wordlessly.

Suzanne slapped her book shut and sat up. "There, I'm done with that book," she announced. "That's the fifth book I've read this week."

"Wow!" exclaimed Twila. "You'd better never say you're over-worked if you have time to read five books in one week's time."

"Oh, I'm a fast reader," Suzanne excused herself. "Mother," she went on in the same breath, "can we make hot chocolate? It's a hot-chocolatey sort of evening."

Mother glanced at the clock. "Yes, I think we have time before bed. Make enough for everyone though."

Robbie cheered. "Hot chocolate! Good! I want marshmallows!" He ran into the kitchen after Suzanne.

Tanisha had also followed Robbie into the kitchen, where Twila could hear Suzanne cheerfully organizing the whole affair. She got out a kettle and carefully measured a cup of milk for each family member. Robbie pulled up a stool to watch, and Suzanne let him pour in the chocolate powder mix. "Now," she announced. "We're going to let the milk heat. Let's get the coffee mugs. Robbie and Tanisha, I'll get them down from the cupboard for you, and you can put them on the table."

"I want marshmallows," Robbie reminded her.

"If you want marshmallows, you need to go ask Mother if we have any," Suzanne replied.

Robbie ran to ask Mother, and Suzanne and Tanisha carried the mugs to the table.

A short time later the family gathered around the table, sipping cups of hot chocolate. The wind howled outside, but it was so cozy around the table that Twila felt her earlier disappointment slip away. It would have been fun to go to Grandma's, but it was also nice to sit comfortably with her family around the table on a cold night.

Robbie got his wished-for marshmallows. He dropped a big one into his cup, where it floated on the top of his drink. With his spoon, he pushed it down into the warm liquid, and then giggled delightedly when the marshmallow popped back to the surface.

Tanisha sipped her hot chocolate and chattered to Robbie. "I've got lots of hot chocolate. I've got more than you, and I'm going to drink it all gone."

Robbie looked at his cup and then over at Tanisha's. He shrugged. "I got same as you. I've got a bunch!" He happily continued dunking his marshmallow.

Tanisha sipped her hot chocolate and ate four big marshmallows. She would have taken another one, but Dad noticed and told her she had enough. Twila watched Tanisha drain the last of her hot drink and thought that whatever had bothered Tanisha earlier seemed to have been forgotten.

Twila looked contentedly around the table at each one of her family. She was thankful for Dad and Mother who loved and cared for them and for the friendship of an older sister and the fun of the younger girls. She was glad for the spice that a little brother added. And she was also glad for Tanisha and the spot she was filling in their family. With such a loving family surrounding her, she could even feel thankful for the snow.

CHAPTER FIVE

The End of the Honeymoon

Twila woke with a start. She had heard Marilyn get up earlier but had fallen back to sleep. She glanced at her alarm clock and realized it would be time for breakfast in just a few minutes. She got up, quickly pulled on her clothes, and combed her hair. The others were already finding their places at the table when she entered the dining room.

"Good morning, lazy!" Marilyn greeted her cheerfully.

"Morning!" Twila returned sheepishly. She noticed the full egg basket on the kitchen counter and knew that Marilyn had done her chores for her. "Where's Dad?" she asked.

"Dad had some work he wanted to get done on the Carlson job," Mother answered. "He left early this morning but plans to be back by noon." She placed several boxes of cereal on the table.

Twila ruffled Robbie's hair as she sat down beside him. Across the table, Tanisha was squirming in her chair and poking Rita with her fork. Mother took the fork as she walked by and went to sit at her own spot. "Okay, let's pray," Mother said cheerfully.

After prayer, each girl picked the kind of cereal she wanted and poured it into her bowl. Rita held a box of cornflakes in her hand and looked at the other kinds, debating which cereal she wanted. "Rita, take what you want of those cornflakes and then please pass them on!" exclaimed Suzanne.

Rita hesitated a moment longer and then said, "I guess I'll mix cornflakes and puffed wheat together."

Twila grinned at her little sister. "Yeah, that's what you usually do!" She turned to take the milk Suzanne had passed to her and saw Tanisha grab a box of Cheerios and dump half of its contents into her bowl. Her bowl filled and overflowed onto the table. Tanisha laughed and looked around to see if anyone was watching her. Disgusted, Twila pretended not to notice the mess.

Mother got another bowl for Tanisha and gave her a moderate amount of cereal from the mess on the table. She poured milk into the bowl and set it before Tanisha.

Usually Tanisha was the first one done with her food and demanding more. But this morning she took only a few bites. She spent the rest of her time poking and kicking Rita. Mother moved Tanisha out of reach of Rita and took the spoon and started feeding Tanisha. Tanisha accepted the bites of food, but made faces at anyone who looked her way. When Connie got up to refill the plastic water pitcher, Tanisha snatched Mother's table knife from beside her plate and jabbed Connie as she went by.

"Ouch!" exclaimed Connie. "You quit that!" She gave Tanisha a thump on the head with the empty pitcher. It was obvious the little thump hadn't hurt her, but Tanisha grabbed her head with both hands and howled.

Mother turned Tanisha around in her chair and said firmly, "Listen, you leave people alone!" She turned to Connie. "And you know better than to hit her!"

Connie sniffed and rubbed her arm. "Well, it hurt when she poked me. And I didn't mean to hit her. I did it without thinking."

"I know," soothed Mother. "But the best way to teach others to be kind is to be kind ourselves."

Connie nodded and went to the sink to refill the pitcher, still rubbing her arm. When she came back, she made a wide loop around Tanisha.

Is Tanisha finally showing her troubled side? wondered Twila, with a pang of dismay. She quickly shrugged the thought aside. All children acted like this once in a while, didn't they?

After breakfast Mother said, "I'll do the dishes, girls. Tanisha, you help me. Start by clearing the table."

Tanisha eyed Mother darkly for a moment, but reluctantly rose from her chair to help. Slowly she began collecting the bowls, carrying one at a time to the counter.

"Tanisha, I want you to stack all the bowls in one stack and then carry them over," Mother instructed.

Tanisha threw Mother another dark look. She went back to the table and stacked two bowls together and carried them to the counter. Then she got two more, all the while keeping track of Mother to see what she would do. Tanisha seemed disappointed when Mother appeared not to notice her disobedience.

When Tanisha finished with the bowls, Mother said, "Now you may pour all the extra water in the cups into the pitcher, and I'll pour it down the drain." Tanisha took two of the fullest cups of water and carried them to the sink and dumped them into Mother's hot dishwater, cooling it.

"No, Tanisha! Pour the water into the pitcher."

As Twila swept the kitchen and dining room floor, she observed that Tanisha found a wrong way to do every task Mother gave her. When she told Tanisha to put the milk in the refrigerator, Tanisha put the cereal in instead. When Mother told her to leave the tablecloth on the table, she took it off. At long last her little chores were done. "Thank you, Tanisha," Mother said evenly and stooped to give her a hug. "You may go play now."

Tanisha wandered into the living room where Robbie was playing. Before long, there was a piercing shriek and then loud wailing. Mother hastily left the sink and went to settle the fight. These fights between Robbie and Tanisha were getting more numerous all the time. It was hard to know who really was at fault. Robbie would cry while Tanisha looked on with wide, innocent eyes and a logical explanation that always made Robbie look silly or guilty.

Marilyn grinned wryly at Twila. "Well, I think our honeymoon with Tanisha is over."

Twila pondered that. "Is the problem Robbie? Or Tanisha? Or is it both?"

"Well," Marilyn countered, "Robbie's six years younger than Rita and used to getting a lot of attention. And he's never really had anyone to share toys with, at least not on a permanent basis. It's understandable if he's a little jealous of Tanisha. It looks to me though that sometimes Tanisha deliberately tries to upset him. You saw how she acted at the breakfast table. Tanisha doesn't just have problems with Robbie. She struggles in other areas too."

"Well, I sure hope they learn to play nicely soon." Twila sighed. "I'm tired of listening to all that screaming. It isn't like Robbie to get so upset. He's usually pretty easygoing."

Marilyn put a CD into the stereo. "We just need to be patient. Tanisha's still learning to know us. And think of all she's been through. What would it be like to have a mother who neglected and abandoned you? Mother told me that Tanisha wasn't regularly fed milk, even as a baby. Her family would just put Kool-Aid or soda pop in a bottle for her." Marilyn pushed the button, and music floated through the house.

Twila was shocked. "Poor little thing! That's a terrible way to treat a baby."

Marilyn agreed. "It's really sad. But maybe Tanisha's parents didn't know you shouldn't feed a baby pop. It's hard to imagine that there are people who actually don't know that kind of thing. But Mother said it does happen."

Twila threw a toy into the toy box. "Whatever the reason she's being so naughty now, I suppose we need to remember how we thought Tanisha was too good before, like . . . she wasn't real or something. I guess we shouldn't be too hard on her."

Mother came through the room, leading Robbie and Tanisha by the hand. "Come," she said cheerfully. "You can both help Mother do the dishes. Robbie, why don't you rinse? Tanisha, you can dry."

She pushed some stools up to the cupboard and got the two preschoolers situated to help her. But Tanisha wasn't content to dry dishes and was soon standing with Robbie on his stool. She sloshed water and it spilled onto Robbie, flooding the stool. Robbie slipped and fell to the floor with a howl.

Mother helped him up and tried to comfort him. "She pushed me!" Robbie sobbed.

Tanisha was quick to defend herself. "I did not push him. He fell all by himself."

Mother called, "Marilyn, come get Robbie and change his clothes while I finish these dishes."

Tanisha stayed to help Mother. Water sloshed down the front of the cupboard and onto Tanisha. At this rate, she'd be needing dry clothes too. When she carelessly dumped dishes into the rack, Mother cautioned, "Careful, Tanisha, or you'll break a dish."

A moment later another dish clattered into the rack, and Twila heard the unmistakable sound of breaking.

"Tanisha!" Mother scolded.

"But I didn't mean to!" whined Tanisha.

Mother said firmly, "You'll have to get down now. I told you to be careful, and you didn't listen." Connie was walking through the kitchen, and Mother called to her. "It's a nice day and most of the snow from that last storm has melted. Take Tanisha outside and give her a ride on the swing. It will do you both good to get some fresh air."

"Come, Tanisha," Connie said cheerfully. "I'll push you on the swing."

Previously, Tanisha had loved getting pushed on the swing, but now she walked slowly to the door, complaining, "I don't want to swing. I don't like that swing."

"Come on," coaxed Connie. "I'll push you nice and high."

Connie reached down to help her with her boots, but Tanisha jerked them away. Walking away from Connie, she slowly slid her feet into her boots. Connie held the door open for Tanisha, and together they went outside. The April weather was so warm they didn't need jackets.

It wasn't long before the two girls came back in, Tanisha sobbing tearlessly and Connie wearing a stricken expression.

"I don't know what happened, but she suddenly fell out of the swing."

"I did not fall!" shouted Tanisha. "You pushed me. On purpose too!"

Connie was on the verge of tears. "I didn't mean to. I was just trying to give her a nice ride. She always said before that she likes when I push her nice and high."

"I'm sure you didn't mean to," Mother comforted Connie. "Shhh, Tanisha! Stop crying and tell me where you're hurt." Mother tried to put an arm around Tanisha, but she jerked away. She kept wailing and insisting that Connie was being mean to her.

"Come," said Mother firmly. "Let's go to the couch and read a book."

Tanisha came reluctantly but refused to sit on Mother's lap. She sat stiffly beside her and wouldn't pay any attention or even look at the pictures. Her expression changed from angry to blank.

Finally Mother laid the book aside and pulled the little girl onto her lap. She tried to cuddle Tanisha, but she only sat stiff and rigid. When Mother tried to talk to her, she just sat there with an empty look on her face.

Finally Mother sat her on the couch. "I want you to stay here for a while," she told Tanisha pleasantly but firmly.

As the morning slipped by, Twila marveled at Mother's calm patience. Tanisha had been difficult and disobedient all morning long.

"Doesn't it make you upset, the way Tanisha is acting?" Twila asked Mother. Mother placed a stack of towels in the bathroom closet and shut the door before she answered.

"Yes, it does," Mother admitted. "But remember how hard life was for her with her birth family, and then suddenly she was moved from her aunt's house to live with a foster family she didn't know. After being there only a few months, she moved to our place. She *should* be upset. You girls would be too, if you were suddenly moved from home to home by strangers. Remembering this helps me to accept her as she is right now."

Mother moved to the doorway, still speaking. "We know we'll provide a safe place for Tanisha, but she doesn't know that yet. She doesn't trust us. And why should she? She's never met anyone reliable yet. Building trust takes time. And until she learns to trust us, she will continue to be difficult. She really needs our love and patience right now."

Twila gave the bathroom mirror another polish with her paper towel. She sighed. "I suppose you're right. I sure get tired of how obstinate she can be. But she can be cute sometimes! Like the other day when she tied that doll blanket on her head and clomped around the house in Marilyn's Sunday shoes. She looked so funny!"

"Yes," agreed Mother. "There's a lovable, imaginative little girl hidden away inside of her. We need to keep looking for the sweet little girl part of her that she hides so well."

Twila threw her used paper towel in the trash and picked up her rag and started scrubbing the sink. "Are Dale and Sarah Glick coming for Sunday dinner tomorrow?"

Mother paused at the door. "Yes. I was hoping we could get most of the cleaning and some baking done this morning. This afternoon I really need to transplant those tomatoes I started. When you're done cleaning the bathroom, I'd like you to mix up a German chocolate cake and make some tapioca pudding. Use Aunt Faith's recipe for the tapioca. That's the one we all like best. It's in the recipe box."

Twila hurried to finish cleaning. Maybe she could get the baking done before lunch. As soon as she was done, she went out to the kitchen to bake the cake. When Robbie saw her pull the mixer out, he came running. "I wanna help!" he insisted.

Twila groaned inwardly. She wouldn't be breaking any speed records with Robbie in the kitchen. "All right, you can help," she said rather shortly. "But you keep your fingers out of my batter, or I'm not going to let you lick the beaters."

Robbie pushed a stool over and scrambled up to watch. Twila dumped in the ingredients and obligingly let Robbie turn the mixer on and off. When the cake was thoroughly mixed, she poured the batter into a pan and gave Robbie the promised beaters. He licked them happily while Twila got out a kettle along with milk, eggs, and tapioca to make the pudding.

Marilyn came into the kitchen and stirred the soup simmering on the stove. She pulled out a frying pan and set it on the stove to make grilled cheese sandwiches to go with the soup.

"Hey, I was going to make tapioca!" Twila objected.

"Sorry, but you're going to have to wait until after lunch. Dad's going to be home soon, and we need to have lunch ready when he gets here. Could you please help me butter this bread so I can get done faster?"

Twila glanced at the clock. "Oh, it is that late? Just a minute. Let me get a knife, and I'll help you."

Mother came into the kitchen holding Tanisha by the hand. She pulled out a chair and sat Tanisha on it. "You stay there until Dad comes home," she instructed. Tanisha, still out of sorts, sat down sulkily.

Mother filled the sink with soapy water and started washing the baking dishes. On her chair, Tanisha stiffened and slid to the floor. Mother calmly and firmly put Tanisha back on her chair. But Tanisha slid off the chair so often that finally Mother just ignored her and let her lie there.

Twila felt disgust as she glanced at Tanisha lying on the floor. She knew if Robbie were acting like that, Mother would spank him. But she also knew Mother was respecting the policies of foster care that did not allow that type of discipline.

Mother started singing and the girls joined in, trying to ignore the defiant little girl lying on the floor. Occasionally Tanisha gave a kick as if to let Mother know she was still there and that she was not going to obey.

The phone rang, interrupting their singing. Mother turned to Marilyn. "Could you get the phone, please? My hands are wet."

Marilyn picked up the phone. The person on the other end of the line seemed to be doing most of the talking. Marilyn gave only an occasional reply.

Marilyn hung up the phone and said, "That was Drusilla Yoder. She just wanted to tell us how much she enjoys having Tanisha in her preschool class at church. She said Tanisha's very sweet and obedient. She's already learned most of the songs and says her verse perfectly every Sunday."

Twila glanced down at Tanisha lying on the floor. The little girl had suddenly gone very still, and there was a triumphant gleam in her eyes. Mother must have caught the look too, because before Marilyn could go on, Mother shook her head slightly, indicating that it would be best to change the subject.

Mother began another song and went on with her dishwashing. The girls blended their voices with Mother's, Twila singing alto and Marilyn high tenor. As they sang, Twila puzzled over the look she'd seen in Tanisha's eyes. She wondered if Drusilla would really think her pupil was so wonderful if she could see how Tanisha was acting at the moment.

As Mother was finishing up the last of the dishes, the three middle sisters entered the kitchen. All three girls were flushed and windblown from playing outside. "I'm *so* hungry!" Suzanne exclaimed, shutting the door with a bang.

"Well, we'll be ready to eat soon," said Mother. "Wash your hands, girls. Then, Suzanne, you may run down and get a jar of pickles. Connie and Rita, I want you to set the table."

When Dad's truck pulled in the lane a few minutes later, Tanisha jumped up from the floor. As Dad walked in, she flung herself at him, shrieking, "Daddy, Daddy!" She wrapped her arms around his leg so tightly he could hardly walk.

He laughed and scooped her up and gave her a hug. A moment later he put her down. "Go sit at the table," he told her. "I need to wash up."

Tanisha bounced to the table and sat down. Her nasty mood had vanished. *I guess it's a good thing she likes someone around here*, Twila thought. *It doesn't seem as though she likes Mother and us girls overly much.*

After Dad led in prayer and the food had been passed around, he cleared his throat and looked at Mother. "How would you like to have new flooring for the dining room?"

Mother looked perplexed. "I'd like it, of course. But I thought we had decided to wait awhile for new flooring."

"I know. But Mr. Carlson stopped in today while I was putting trim in his new house. He told me his wife decided she doesn't like the linoleum they bought. They're going to pick out something different, and he said we could buy what they chose first for half price. I told him I'd talk to you and let him know if we're interested."

"What color is it?" Mother wondered.

"It's a marbled gray color. Very practical and wouldn't show dirt. It's not quite the same as the flooring you picked out in the store one time to show me, but it's very similar."

"Well, it's up to you," Mother replied. "It sounds like something I could be happy with. We'll need to replace the flooring in the dining room sometime anyway."

"Well, then," said Dad, "I'll tell him we'll take it."

Lunch over, Mother went and tucked the two youngest into bed. Since Twila still had the cake to ice and the tapioca pudding to finish, she offered to wash the dishes. Mother suggested she wash the kitchen floor too, and told Marilyn and Suzanne to come out to the greenhouse with her. The tomatoes, flowers, and some other vegetables for their produce garden needed transplanting. Connie and Rita went with Dad in the truck to pick up the new linoleum and buy some other flooring supplies.

Happy to have the quiet house to herself, Twila worked steadily in the kitchen. An hour and a half later, she was done. She flipped the kitchen light off and went through the rest of the house, picking up a few toys, straightening the bookshelf, and dusting a chair that one of the younger girls had forgotten. Satisfied that the house was ready for company, she slipped on her flip-flops and went out to help in the greenhouse. Already, flats of flowers and vegetables were filling the shelves.

"Wow, those geraniums you transplanted a week ago really look nice!" Twila commented as she surveyed the progress that had been made.

"Mother thinks it's that new kind of potting soil we're using this year." Suzanne brushed some hair out of her eyes, leaving a black smudge. "It seems to make the plants just leap out of the soil."

For the next couple of hours Mother and the girls laughed and talked while they worked. By the time they were done, it was time to get supper ready.

"Well, thank you, girls!" Mother said warmly. "It's a good feeling to have that all done. I usually like to have the transplanting done by now, but with Tanisha coming, I've been extra busy."

Dad drove in the lane, and they all went out to see the new linoleum. Robbie and Tanisha had awakened from their naps some time earlier. Robbie had been playing in the sandbox, but when Tanisha started playing there too, he left. He had wandered over to his tricycle and rode that instead. He came running to see what the others were looking at, but Tanisha stayed at the sandbox, seemingly oblivious to the rest of the family gathered around the truck. Robbie climbed up the side of the truck, stood on the tire, and clutched the truck bed with his arms.

Dad unrolled the flooring slightly so they could see what it looked like. Mother was pleased. "I really like that. It should look very nice in the dining room." The girls voiced their approval and delight, talking excitedly of how nice the dining room would look when it was installed.

The next morning, everyone was up early to get ready for church and put the finishing touches on the Sunday dinner.

Mother laid out Tanisha's clothes and told Twila to help her get ready for church. Twila tried, but Tanisha refused any help. She wouldn't even let Twila zip her dress. And then, though Twila tried to hurry her, Tanisha moved with irksome slowness. She found a long way to do everything. Twila tried hard to swallow her irritation, and when at last Tanisha was dressed, she said cheerfully, "There now, you look all nice and ready for church!"

She tried to hug Tanisha, but the little girl stiffened and pulled away. *She's getting as prickly as a porcupine,* thought Twila. What had happened to the affectionate little girl who so lavishly passed out hugs when she had first come to live with them?

"Come. Dad's calling. We need to get out in the van," urged Twila. "Oh, and you'd better put your sweater on. It's chilly this morning."

But Tanisha turned away. "No! I'm not wearing a sweater. Don't need one."

"But you'll get cold. It's chilly outside." Twila held up the sweater and tried to persuade her to put it on. But she refused.

Mother came to the door to see what was taking so long. Twila explained to Mother, who also tried to get Tanisha to put her sweater on. But Tanisha flatly refused.

"All right," Mother said. "It's getting late. You'll just have to go without."

As they walked into church, a chilly breeze made Twila shiver through her sweater. But Tanisha marched along with the rest of them as though she didn't feel the cold. Twila wondered what people must be thinking of them for letting Tanisha come to church without a jacket or sweater.

A few people were standing inside the door. Two of the church ladies shook hands with Mother, and then one of them turned to Tanisha. "Good morning, Tanisha. Where's your sweater? Isn't it a little chilly for you?"

Tanisha smiled sweetly up at her. "Oh, I wanted to wear a sweater, but Mother said I didn't need one." The ladies' eyebrows shot up, and it was clear what they thought. The song leader was announcing the number of the opening hymn, so they all turned and quickly walked into church.

Twila helped sing, but the words of the song barely registered. She was inwardly fuming about Tanisha's blatant lie. Now those ladies thought Mother was being mean, making Tanisha go without a sweater when it was still cold outside. Not until the sermon began could Twila push away her embarrassment and humiliation.

Tanisha sat as still as a mouse beside Mother. She looked like a perfect model of good behavior. *It's no wonder people like Drusilla think Tanisha is so good!* Twila thought. It was very confusing.

When it was time to go to Sunday school, Twila got up and went to her class. She made an effort to quit mulling over the morning with Tanisha and focus on the Sunday school lesson.

After church was over, Twila stood talking with the other girls her age. Tanisha came up and stood beside Twila. Remembering how she had pulled away from her before church, Twila rather cautiously took Tanisha's hand. To her amazement, Tanisha leaned cozily against her. Beth, one of Twila's friends, bent down to talk to the little girl. "How are you this morning? I like your dress! That pink looks very pretty on you."

Before long, Beth was sitting on the bench holding Tanisha while the little girl smiled engagingly and chattered nonstop. "I like this dress too," she said. "And Mother is going to make me a purple dress and a yellow dress and a blue dress."

"Oh, wow!" exclaimed Beth. "You're getting lots of new dresses." The other girls nearby had stopped talking among themselves and were listening to the conversation too.

Twila felt a mounting resentment toward Tanisha. How could one little girl have the ability to so completely control the conversation? And what she was saying wasn't even true! Mother had already made her several dresses and had no plans to make any more for a while. Twila wanted to correct Tanisha's statements, but the other girls were listening so raptly to what she was saying that it seemed rude and petty to interrupt. How could Tanisha be so nice at church? She certainly hadn't been displaying her charms at home lately! At least not to Mother and the other girls. And all these lies! Twila seethed.

But Beth was giving the little girl a squeeze and saying, "I think I'm going to take you home with me! Want to come to my house?"

"Oh, yes!" Tanisha beamed.

Seeing the rest of her family was ready to go, Twila rather abruptly took Tanisha's hand and led her down the aisle.

In the van, the Hammond family discussed the church service, exchanging news and bits of information they had learned that morning.

"I can't believe it! I can't believe it!" Tanisha exclaimed suddenly. "That man standing up in front of the church was swearing. He said 'Holy Spirit'!" She turned to Mother and said accusingly, "I thought you said it was bad to swear. That man swore two times! Right in church! I heard him! I just can't believe it!"

Twila wanted to laugh at Tanisha's amazement. But she hid her smile while Dad explained to Tanisha, "You're right. It's wrong to swear. God made us, and He's done so much for us that we want to speak respectfully of Him. It's wrong to use the words *God* and *Jesus* carelessly. God is holy, so we don't want to use the word *holy* when we're not talking about God. But Brother Don was not swearing. He was talking about the Holy Spirit, who is part of God. The Holy Spirit is the One who speaks to our hearts and tells us what is right or wrong to do. The Holy Spirit and our conscience help us make decisions and choose right things."

Dad clicked on his left turn signal to pull into the driveway. "Do you understand what I mean?" he asked Tanisha.

Tanisha nodded and crawled out of the van. Twila wondered how much she understood. There was so much Tanisha didn't know. Mother and Dad used every opportunity to teach her about

God, but it was hard to know sometimes how much Tanisha was absorbing.

In the house, Mother and the girls put dinner on the table. Dale and Sarah Glick came as planned, and the Hammonds had a pleasant afternoon with the elderly couple.

But as the afternoon wore on, Twila observed Tanisha with growing bewilderment. She played with Robbie and her younger sisters as nicely as could be. She talked and laughed and shared her toys. She sat on Mother's lap and sweetly did whatever Mother asked of her—something she hadn't done much of recently.

Twila noticed Mother watching Tanisha throughout the afternoon with a thoughtful expression.

Just who is this little girl? Twila wondered.

The following week was filled to the brim with school, work, and other activities. On Tuesday evening Twila's family went along with other families from their church to sing for the elderly people at an assisted living home. On Friday evening they went to a church family's home for supper.

Twila told Marilyn, "I sure hope nothing comes up to ruin our plans for Saturday!" The first weekend of May was always the big garage sale day for the town of Bentley, about an hour's drive away. Mother and the girls went every year if they could.

Now it was Saturday morning, and Mother and the girls were driving to Bentley. Twila was happy. It would be a fun day just for girls. Robbie had cheerfully stayed at home to do "men stuff" with Dad.

As they neared the Bentley subdivision, garage sale signs began to pop up. They made their way along, stopping at many different places.

It seemed that people took one look at all the Hammond girls and were quick to offer any dolls they had for sale. At one place, Rita nudged Connie and whispered, "Look at that big doll!" The two girls stood looking with delight at a huge four-foot-tall Raggedy Ann doll.

The owner noticed. "Would you like that doll? Here, you may have it for free! I don't want it back in my house again." She picked up the doll and held it out to Rita. Rita looked longingly at the doll and then over at Mother.

Twila looked at Marilyn and rolled her eyes. "No way!" she whispered. Marilyn's eyes mirrored Twila's feelings. If Mother let Rita have it, that dreadful doll would fill up the house!

Twila was relieved when Mother smiled and said politely, "I'm sorry, but we just don't have room for a doll that size in our vehicle. But thanks anyway." Looking disappointed at losing her chance to get rid of the doll, the lady set it back down in its chair once again.

Back in the van a few minutes later, Marilyn sank into her seat and exclaimed, "Whew! Mother, I'm sure glad you didn't let Rita and Connie have that horrid doll! We have enough trouble keeping the house clean without an enormous doll adding to the clutter."

Suzanne climbed in over a step stool Mother had bought and sat down in the back seat. "I think it would have been fun to have a great big doll like that."

"I know. I think so too," said Rita wistfully.

"It sure was cute!" Connie added.

"I didn't see anything cute about it," said Twila. "And besides, you girls would have played with it for just a few days and then been tired of it."

The morning passed quickly. Each of the girls found at least one thing they wanted to take home with them. Mother kept Tanisha close beside her, and for the most part, she was cooperative. By noon the girls were hungry and tired of shopping. Mother pulled away from the last garage sale and said, "I think we'll call that good enough for today. We'll stop somewhere and get something to eat, and then we'll head home. Now, if we can find our way out of here."

Suzanne laughed and looked around the crowded van. "I don't think we have room for much more stuff anyhow."

Mother pulled up to an intersection and exclaimed, "Do you girls remember which way we came? For some reason I'm kind of tangled up with my directions."

Marilyn looked both ways. "I'm pretty sure you need to take a right."

Mother turned right, and a little later she turned left. But the longer they drove, the more unfamiliar everything looked. Twila and Marilyn tried to help Mother out, but they didn't agree on which way to go, and neither of them were sure themselves which was the right way.

Finally Mother said, "I'm hopelessly confused! If we see a store or a gas station, we'll have to stop and ask for directions."

Mother was about to make another left turn when Tanisha suddenly spoke up. "No, Mother, it's not that way. We need to go the other way."

Mother looked surprised. "Are you sure, Tanisha?"

Tanisha nodded emphatically. She seemed so confident that Mother laughed and said, "Well, I guess I might as well try it your way. We can't get any more lost than we already are."

Suzanne sniffed and turned to Twila, saying under her breath, "I can't believe she knows how to get us out of here. She's too little. I bet she couldn't find her way out of a wet paper bag!"

Twila was skeptical too, but at every stop sign Tanisha confidently told Mother which way to turn. Soon landmarks started to look familiar, and before long they were out on the main road.

Mother and the girls were amazed. "How did you know where to go?" asked Rita.

Tanisha replied smugly, " 'Cause I'm smart."

Mother found a place to buy sandwiches. After they had eaten lunch, they stopped at a gas station to refuel the van, and then they went home.

Twila helped unload the garage sale purchases. She and Mother were bringing in the last two bags when Twila asked the question she'd been wondering about the whole way home. "How did Tanisha know how to get out of that subdivision when the rest of us were totally messed up?"

Mother chuckled. "I suppose part of it is just natural ability. Some people just have the knack of knowing where they are at all times. And probably part of it is that children who've been through traumatic experiences tend to be extra alert to what's going on around them."

Twila nodded, understanding. In the house, she took her bag of stuff and headed for her room. She dumped her things out on the bed and happily browsed through them. She was holding up a sweater when Marilyn entered the room with her own bag of possessions.

"I just love this sweater!" Twila exclaimed. "The black color and style make it look so dressy. I want to wash it so I can wear it to church tomorrow."

"If it's not too warm," Marilyn returned. "The last couple days have been so warm we hardly need sweaters." She fished a book out of her bag. "I'm so glad I found this book!" It was the second in a series. Twila knew Marilyn had been hoping for a long time to find it somewhere.

Twila hugged a thick tablet of drawing paper to her chest. "I was so pleased to find this, and I can't wait to try it out." The paper had never been used; a plastic sleeve still protected it.

Marilyn pulled on a pair of thick, warm gloves. "I really like these gloves. I don't need them now, of course, but I'll be glad for them next winter."

Twila looked over at Marilyn's gloves. "I'm jealous. I wish I'd found them first. They're so pretty."

"Well, I found them first, and you're not getting them." Marilyn grinned.

"No big deal! You can have them. I don't need them anyway." Twila swept all her stuff from the top of her nightstand and added, "But I do really like this dresser scarf I found. It's just the perfect size for my nightstand."

Marilyn finished putting her things away while Twila arranged her nightstand. When she was finished, she stepped back to look at her work. She moved her lamp to the right a little more and her mug of pens to the left. Satisfied with how it looked and content with her day, Twila went out to the living room to join the rest of her family.

CHAPTER SIX

A Deep Black Hole

Twila entered Tanisha's room, holding a bucket of water and window spray in one hand, a stool in the other hand, and a roll of paper towels tucked under her arm. She set down the stool near the window at the head of Tanisha's bed. As she did so, the roll of paper towels slipped out from under her arm and went rolling underneath the bed.

Twila got down on her hands and knees to retrieve it, lifting the blanket to get a better look. She paused. What was that musty, moldy smell? Leaning closer, she was shocked to see half of a cake lying under the bed, with blue-gray mold growing across the top of it. Beside it lay a package of hot dog buns that apparently had been put there more recently, because they still looked quite fresh.

Twila sat back on her heels, feeling repulsed. Who would do such a thing? Tanisha? But what was the point of stashing food under a bed and letting it rot?

It couldn't stay there, that was for sure! Twila grabbed the wastebasket sitting by the dresser and gingerly fished the hot dog buns and cake out from under the bed. She dumped the cake into the wastebasket and carried it and the package of buns down to the kitchen.

"Mother, just look what I found in Tanisha's bedroom!"

Mother and Connie turned from where they were peeling potatoes at the sink. Connie wrinkled her nose at the moldy cake. "Ugh, where did you find that? It's gross!"

Mother inspected the contents of the wastebasket. "I thought I smelled something last evening when I put Tanisha to bed, but I couldn't seem to locate it."

"It was under Tanisha's bed. Do you think she put it there?" Twila wondered.

"Yes, I'm sure she did," Mother replied.

"Didn't Mrs. Gunther tell us Tanisha didn't have enough to eat? Is that why she hid this food?" asked Twila.

"Yes, that's true. Tanisha didn't have enough to eat. The food she did have was things like crackers, bread, and sometimes boxed cereals. And that was all—no milk, eggs, fruit, or fresh things like that," said Mother. "Apparently she hid that food because she doesn't realize that we'll take good care of her and that we'll always provide her with plenty of food."

"Oh, Mother," said Twila. "That poor child!"

Connie interrupted her. "Is that why she gets mad when you don't let her have more than two helpings of food at mealtimes?"

"Yes, it seems when she sees food, she's afraid it might be the last meal she gets. Apparently she snuck this food out of the kitchen to save for a day when the adults in her life fail her and she has to go hungry."

"But, Mother," protested Twila. "Why would she save food that spoils? A cake!"

"I think she's trying to survive," Mother said. "Children who survive the kind of neglect Tanisha faced have to do some strange things in order to stay alive. It doesn't make sense to those of us who have never gone hungry. But to those who have, it makes perfect sense."

Mother turned to Connie. "Run outside and get Tanisha for me. She's on the swing. I want to talk to her."

When Tanisha came in, Mother showed her what Twila had found under her bed. A look of pain and fear flashed across the small girl's face. Twila was surprised. The only genuine emotion she had seen in Tanisha since she had come was anger. But for a moment, she looked so vulnerable that Twila wanted to snatch her close and hug her tight.

Mother got out a small ziplock bag and filled it with mixed nuts and dried fruit. She sat down on a chair and pulled Tanisha onto her lap. She said gently, "You've been hungry lots of times, haven't you, Tanisha?" The little girl only sat stiffly and said nothing.

Mother went on. "I wonder if you're afraid that sometime you won't have anything to eat. I wonder if you saved that food in case you get hungry and your tummy hurts like it did at your Auntie Rasheeda's house. That must not have felt good, to be hungry all the time."

Mother gently tipped Tanisha's chin up so she could look into her eyes. "If I was a hungry little girl and there was no food in the house, I'd be scared too."

For a moment Tanisha's eyes flickered with interest. She asked, "You would?"

"Yes," replied Mother. "I'd be very scared that I'd never have food to eat again. Twila and Connie would be scared too." Tanisha's eyes turned to the girls. She looked surprised.

Mother picked up the bag of nuts and dried fruit. "But remember, we'll always have food for you to eat. But in case you ever get hungry, we'll put this bag of food in your bedroom. If you get hungry, you can get it out and eat it. This is food that won't spoil."

Mother took Tanisha to her room and suggested she put the bag in a drawer. For a moment Tanisha stood still, as if deciding. Then she crossed the room and tucked the bag under her pillow. Tanisha looked up at Mother, and for a brief moment Twila saw gratitude on the small girl's face.

Mother and Tanisha left the room. As Twila scrubbed the bedroom windows, she felt a new compassion for Tanisha. What would it be like to be hungry and deprived as Tanisha had been? She determined to have a new love and patience for Tanisha. She resolved that she wouldn't let Tanisha's behavior get under her skin. Surely if they loved her enough, it would make a difference in this little girl's life.

Twila dried the storm window and put it back in place. She got the stool and hung up the new curtains Mother had made for Tanisha's room. She carefully straightened the curtains and stood back to make sure they were hanging correctly.

In spite of being very busy, Mother had been determined to finish the curtains for Tanisha's room. It was one more way to show Tanisha she loved her, despite the little girl's increasingly troubling behavior. Now the curtains hung on the rods, crisp and fresh-looking, adding a cheerful touch to the bedroom. Any little girl should be delighted with such curtains.

Tanisha came into her room. Ignoring the new curtains, she went straight to her bed and peeked under the pillow to make sure the little bag of food was still there. She pulled it out and looked at it for a moment before tucking it back under her pillow. Her small hands carefully smoothed the wrinkles out of the pillowcase. Looking satisfied, she flitted out of the room.

Why didn't I ask her what she thinks of her new curtains? Twila thought. She had been too fascinated, watching Tanisha check on the food under the pillow. Should she bring Tanisha back again to point out the new curtains? *No, I won't bother,* Twila decided. Tanisha hadn't even glanced at them. Lately, it seemed, Tanisha wasn't showing much excitement about anything.

When Marilyn heard about the incident with the spoiled food, she promptly composed a song. That night at supper as Mother placed the steaming bowls of food on the table, Marilyn gaily sang:

"There will always be food on the table,

Food our dear Mother prepares.

Dad works to provide for us;

God lovingly cares for us.

There will always be plenty to spare!"

The other girls picked it up, and soon they were singing too. It was a song they would sing before almost every meal in the months ahead.

After supper Dad took Robbie and Tanisha and strolled through the woods to visit Mr. and Mrs. Graham. He wanted to see if Mr. Graham could help him put in the new dining room flooring. Mother went out to work in the solitude of the greenhouse, and the girls stayed in to do the dishes and sweep the floors.

"It sure is nice to have Tanisha out of the house for a while!" remarked Suzanne. She was sweeping the floor with such vigor that it sent dirt scattering all over the room.

"Suzanne!" Marilyn objected. "That's not a very kind thing to say."

"Oh, don't pretend to be so nice! You feel the exact same way. I know you do!" When Marilyn didn't answer, Suzanne pushed her point. "Right?"

Marilyn plunged a stack of dirty plates into the sink full of soapy water and reluctantly admitted, "It *is* more peaceful when Tanisha isn't around."

Suzanne went on. "I think it's so gross to save food like that and let it rot under your bed! Imagine!"

The other girls were quiet, imagining. "And I get so tired of her screaming." Suzanne's broom clunked on the table leg as she continued her vigorous sweeping. "The other day after school she screamed for two hours. I know, because I timed her. And do you know why she was screaming?"

Twila said wryly, "Which day are you talking about? There was more than one day this week that she threw one of her screaming fits."

"It was yesterday, and it was because Mother told her to go put her shoes in her room. How does she do it?" Suzanne marveled.

"What do you mean, 'How does she do it?' " demanded Marilyn.

"I mean, how does she have the strength and energy to scream for two whole hours?"

Rita giggled. "Suzanne and Connie and I went back in the woods to try it out. We had a real screaming match back there."

"We tried our best, but we didn't last very long," Connie added ruefully. "All we got was sore throats and thumping headaches."

"How does she do it?" insisted Suzanne.

"Well, all I can say is that she's one amazing child!" Marilyn remarked. In spite of her earlier efforts at being kind, Twila heard sarcasm in Marilyn's voice.

"And you know what else makes me mad?" Suzanne said resentfully. "It's the way she acts so nasty when it's just Mother and us girls at home. But let Dad or anyone else come around, and oh, my, she can be as nice as pie!"

Rita asked hesitantly, "Do you think Tanisha does all these things because she has that disease Mother and Dad talked about before she came?"

"Do you mean attachment disorder?" asked Marilyn. "I've been wondering too. I keep wanting to ask Mother, but things have been so hectic around here I haven't had a chance."

"I think," said Twila thoughtfully, "regardless if there's a name for why she acts the way she does, we need to quit focusing on her behavior and think about *why* she's acting that way. At least, that's what Mother says. Today when Mother gave her that bag of food to put under her pillow, she looked so little and scared that I felt sorry for her. She's been through such awful stuff."

Twila got some containers out of the cupboard to put left-overs in. "Mother said Tanisha probably doesn't remember her mother at all, and maybe her dad only a little. Mrs. Gunther told her that the only time he came around was when there was a big party with lots of drugs and alcohol. Think of what all Tanisha was exposed to! What would I be like if I had experienced everything Tanisha has? Most of the time she acts so angry, but I think underneath she must really be scared."

"I know," agreed Marilyn. "I feel sorry for her too. But does she have to treat Mother the way she does? Mother looks so tired all the time, and one day I saw her crying. I try to love Tanisha, but it's hard when she's so mean to Mother. I can't help but wish we could go back to the nice, peaceful times we had before she came."

Suzanne agreed. "We never have nice evenings together as a family anymore. When we try to play games or do things together, Tanisha always spoils it. She pouts or she cheats or she pretends she doesn't know how to play. Last night she told Dad she didn't know how to play the Memory game. But I know she can. I've played Memory with her already, and she beat me every game," Suzanne said disgustedly.

Twila scraped some leftovers into a smaller container and put it in the refrigerator. Still feeling her earlier compassion of the day, she commented, "I think it would be better if we'd focus on the cute things she says and does instead of all the negatives."

Rita wasn't helping with dishes at all, but sat on a stool at the table swinging her legs. "Does Tanisha ever do anything cute?" she wondered.

The girls looked at each other, trying to remember if Tanisha had done anything sweet or funny recently. "I can't think of anything. Can you girls?" Connie asked.

"You know," said Marilyn, "there's one thing she does do nicely—playing with that dollhouse. It's really cute to watch her."

"Maybe," said Suzanne skeptically. "But it still irks me the way she treats Mother."

"Well, school will soon be out, and we'll be able to stay home and help Mother more," Marilyn encouraged. "Then maybe Mother won't look so worn-out."

"It might help." Suzanne didn't sound convinced. She gave the dustpan a kick toward her dirt pile. "But it's so unpleasant at home right now, I'd rather stay in school."

"Oh, that reminds me," Marilyn changed the subject. "We only have four days until the school program, and we still don't have all our new dresses done. Did you even start on yours, Twila?"

Twila shook her head. "Mother doesn't have time to help me sew another one. Besides, I just got two new dresses not long ago. I'll wear one of those."

"Well, if you're not going to make a new one, why don't you help Mother and me finish the rest of our dresses? They're all done except for the zippers and hems."

"I can help put hems in, but you'll have to do the zippers," Twila said. "I tried putting a zipper in my last dress and messed it up so badly that Mother had to throw the zipper away."

"Yes, Marilyn!" Suzanne grinned, her green eyes dancing. "I want *you* to put the zipper in my dress. I don't want ripples up and down my back!" The girls giggled together, momentarily forgetting Tanisha's disturbing behavior. Suzanne shoved the broom into the closet, and the three middle girls skipped out the door to play until bedtime.

The following day after school, Marilyn and Twila got out the dresses to finish them. They searched through the drawers of the sewing cabinet for the tape measure, but couldn't find it. Twila found Mother in the kitchen. "Do you know where the measuring tape is?"

Robbie was pushing his tractor on the floor and making loud engine noises. But he stopped when he heard Twila's question. "I f'ushed it down the potty," he told her.

"You what?" asked Mother.

"I f'ushed it down the potty," repeated Robbie matter-of-factly.

Mother took Robbie's hand. "Come! Show me what you did."

Robbie led Mother to the bathroom and stood in front of the toilet. "I frowed it in the potty, then I f'ushed it and, whoosh! It was all gone!" Robbie gestured with his hands. His dark eyes sparkled.

"Robbie!" scolded Mother. "That was naughty! It could have plugged the toilet and then Dad would have had to take it all apart to get it out. And now Twila doesn't have the tape measure."

Robbie sobered as he looked up at Twila. "I'll buy you another one," he promised solemnly.

"Well," suggested Mother, "maybe you could tell her you're sorry and then help her find a ruler to use instead."

"I'm sorry," Robbie apologized.

Twila hugged the small boy. "I forgive you, Robbie. Let's see if we can find a ruler." Together they rummaged in a drawer until they found an old ruler. Twila took it to the living room where Marilyn was preparing to pin up the hems on the dresses.

"I'm glad Mother got all these zippers put in these dresses today," said Marilyn. "You're not the only one who has trouble sewing them in right."

Twila threaded her needle. She thought of the latest Hammond cousin news and commented, "I think it's so exciting that Sue is dating!"

Marilyn finished pinning the hem of Suzanne's dress and handed it to Twila. "I know. I think it's exciting too," agreed Marilyn. "It's hard to believe I actually have a cousin only three years older than I who is dating. I mean, it doesn't seem long ago that we were little girls playing dolls together!"

For a moment Twila concentrated on keeping her stitches neat and even. She stopped for a moment to smooth out the fabric.

Suzanne wouldn't appreciate puckers in her hem any more than she wanted them in her zipper. After a moment she looked up. "It'll be interesting to meet Sue's boyfriend. Isn't he from the church that Uncle Loren's family used to go to? Aunt Bess says his family is really nice."

Mother came into the living room and picked up Connie's dress. "Supper's in the oven, and the younger children are outside playing. I have a little time, so I might as well help you sew," she said.

She chose a spool of purple thread and snipped a length of it. "So you girls were discussing the new couple?" Mother asked. For the next half hour, Mother and her two oldest daughters chatted comfortably about family, friends, church events, and daily happenings. Every few minutes Mother went to the window to check on Tanisha and Robbie. Their pleasant conversation was suddenly interrupted when Connie burst into the room.

"Mother! Mother! Come to Tanisha's room, quick," Connie gasped. "Something terrible has happened!"

"Oh, no!" groaned Twila. "What now?" In a flash she knew it was something to do with Tanisha's new curtains. Her peaceful feelings vanished in an instant.

When Mother and the girls stepped inside Tanisha's bedroom, they stood speechless with horror. The new curtains Mother had made had jagged chops in them. They hung limply in tattered ribbons.

Marilyn was the first to recover from her shock. "Oh, Mother! Why? Why does she do these terrible things?"

Mother's lips were pressed together, and she said nothing for a long moment. Twila thought she might start crying. Finally Mother sighed. "I think she's trying to say she doesn't trust me, that she's rejecting my love for fear I'll reject her. It seems as though she feels she's just bad anyway, so why should she have anything nice? I know it's hard, girls, but let's try not to be angry with her. We need to determine to keep loving her no matter what."

"But, Mother!" protested Marilyn. "You worked so hard on these curtains, and now this! It's just so . . . so . . ." Marilyn groped for words.

"Do you think she does all this stuff because she has trouble with attachment?" wondered Twila.

"I'm beginning to believe so," said Mother. "I've discussed it with Mrs. Gunther, and she says destructive behavior is typical for a child who has been neglected. The foster care agency thinks a therapist could help decide if we're dealing with a specific disorder. Mrs. Gunther says to give her more time, but to keep her more closely supervised. Dad and I agree with her. We're hoping that all Tanisha needs is a little more time and a whole lot of love."

"Looks to me like we're going to have to watch her even more closely than ever after this," said Marilyn wearily.

Mother nodded. She said, "Marilyn, why don't you take those curtains down right away?"

Twila was glad Mother didn't ask her to take care of the curtains. She was too upset. She went back to the living room to finish the dress she was working on. Connie walked beside her, muttering, "I don't see how we're supposed to keep on loving Tanisha. It's just not possible."

Twila knew she should disagree with Connie, but she wondered the same thing.

Mother turned back to the girls. "What did you say, Connie? That it's not possible to love Tanisha?"

Connie looked guilty. Mother's tired face made Twila wonder if she almost agreed with Connie. Suddenly Mother's shoulders straightened and she said firmly, "It *is* possible to love Tanisha. With God all things are possible. We cannot change the fact that Tanisha chose to chop up her new curtains, but we can still choose to bless her. With God's love in our hearts, we can continue to treat Tanisha with compassion and kindness."

Bless Tanisha? After what she had done? Twila could hardly bring herself to consider Mother's words. It seemed an impossible thing to do.

But in the following days, Twila's heart rose to the challenge, and she began to look for little things she could do for Tanisha. She ironed Tanisha's Sunday dress with extra carefulness and dusted her room. Tanisha probably never noticed many of the things Twila did for her. But it did something for Twila to lovingly serve the little girl even when she did such terrible things.

Mother found her own way to bless Tanisha. The next day after Tanisha had chopped the curtains, Mother called her to the table. "Tanisha!" she exclaimed brightly. "I noticed that you *love* cutting things! I have an old seed catalog here." She handed Tanisha a small pair of children's scissors. "You may cut out pictures of flowers and vegetables and paste them on this sheet of paper."

Tanisha sat still for a long time, and Twila wondered what she would do. At last Tanisha picked up the scissors and began to cut out small squares of words. She glued them onto the paper Mother had provided.

Twila went to her room and flopped across the bed. She rolled over on her back and stared up at the ceiling. *Why?* she wondered. Why was Tanisha so resistant to the very simplest of Mother's suggestions? Why would a child want to cut out words instead of pretty flowers and vegetables? Why couldn't she accept Mother's love?

Twila lay there for a long time. Her mind went this way and that as she sorted through the puzzling questions. What were they doing wrong? Finally, feeling an inner prompting to pray, she knelt down beside the bed and poured out her heart to the Lord. She rose from her knees still feeling perplexed, but with an underlying sense of peace. She knew God was in control.

Friday was the last day of school. Most years, Twila was happy for summer vacation. But this year, because of their family struggles with Tanisha, she did not feel the usual anticipation. Reluctance dragged at her as she went through the motions of cleaning out her desk and putting her things into her book bag. She didn't join in the laughter and noise of the other students. At three o'clock, the teacher dismissed them for the last time, and Twila joined the stream of children filing out of the room. In the hall she grabbed her jacket and lunch box and stepped outside. Mother and her sisters were waiting for her in the van.

"Today Dad made an appointment for you to take your driver's test, Marilyn," Mother said. "It's on Friday, two weeks from now."

"Two weeks!" Marilyn sounded both excited and nervous. "I still have to get in several hours of driving time."

"I know," Mother agreed. "I have some errands to take care of in town after we get home. I thought I'd take you along so you can drive. Twila, I was wondering if you'd be willing to stay home with the girls and Robbie. I'll take Tanisha along with me."

When they got home, Mother assigned work to all the girls. "Twila, I want you to peel potatoes for supper and put them on the stove to cook. Connie, you can take the clothes off the line, and, Suzanne, I want you to fold them. Rita, I noticed you didn't make your bed this morning, so I'm giving you two jobs. Go make your bed right away, and then I want you to take that bucket of table scraps out to the chickens and clean the sink in the bathroom. Once you girls are done with your work, you're free to do whatever you like."

"Mother, where did you say you were going?" Connie looked anxious.

Mother carefully explained, "We're going to town to do some banking for Dad. Then we need to go to the post office, and after that we need to stop at the grocery store. It should only take us a little over an hour. You'll be fine here with Twila," Mother reassured.

Connie glanced at the clock. "You're sure you'll be gone only an hour?"

"Unless something comes up, it shouldn't be much more than that." Mother hugged Connie and turned to Marilyn. "Let's go. I'd like to be back before Dad gets home."

She was about to leave with Tanisha and Marilyn when Robbie started crying. "I want a job too!" he sobbed.

Mother glanced hastily around the kitchen. "Well, Robbie, you can put away the lunch dishes that are in the rack. If you don't know where something belongs, you can ask Twila."

Mother left, and Robbie, beaming his pleasure, got a stool and started putting away the plastic soup bowls, cups, and spoons that Mother and the little children had used for lunch.

When Twila finished the potatoes, she found the book she had been reading and went out to the living room. She curled up in a chair and was soon lost to the world. Occasionally happy laughter floated in through the window from outside, so she didn't worry about the other children.

It wasn't until Connie came in, asking anxiously, "Why isn't Mother home?" that Twila became aware of the passage of time. She glanced at the clock. Mother had been gone only a little over an hour.

"She'll be home soon," Twila said. "It probably just took a little longer than Mother was expecting. Why don't we set the table so we can eat right away when Mother and Dad get home?"

Connie pulled a stack of plates out of the cupboard, and Twila ran downstairs to get a jar of applesauce. Meanwhile Robbie had fallen into a mud puddle, and Rita and Suzanne brought him in.

Suzanne took off his soaked jeans and dried him with a towel while Rita went to his bedroom to get him another set of clothes to wear. She came running out of the bedroom calling, "Twila, Twila! Just look what happened to your picture of Dad! I found it in the trash can in Robbie's room. It's torn, with pen scribbles all over it."

The girls gathered around, exclaiming indignantly over the ruined picture. Twila's heart sank, and tears sprang into her eyes. She was ashamed that she cared so much, but she had worked so hard on that picture!

Suzanne rounded on Robbie. "It must have been you who did it!" she scolded. "It was in the wastebasket in your room. That was terribly naughty!"

Robbie's eyes got big and he stammered, "But I ... I ... I didn't do it!"

"It was in your room!" Rita insisted. "It had to be you who did it! It's wicked to tell lies!"

Seeing that Robbie was near tears, Twila quickly intervened. "Listen, girls, we'd better let Dad and Mother take care of it. We don't know for sure that Robbie did it."

They heard the sound of tires crunching in the lane, and the three middle girls flew out the door. Twila could hear them telling Dad what had happened as they walked back to the house with him.

When the girls showed Dad the damaged drawing, he made very little comment except to ask Robbie a few questions. He laid it on his desk, saying, "I'll discuss this with Mother later."

It was late when Mother came home, and both she and Marilyn looked tired. Tanisha, however, jumped out of the vehicle and ran squealing to Dad.

Marilyn dumped her bags of groceries on the table and glanced at the clock. "Mother, do I have time to take care of the chickens before supper? It's my turn."

"If you hurry," Mother said. She pulled oatmeal out of a bag and placed it in the cupboard.

Twila was itching to find out what had taken Mother and Marilyn so long. She was sure, by their faces, that something had happened. "I'll help so you can get done faster!" she offered. She followed Marilyn out the back door, grabbing the egg basket as she went.

"What took you so long?" Twila asked as Marilyn filled the chicken waterer at the hydrant.

Marilyn sighed. "You'll never believe the things Tanisha did! We went to the bank and the post office first. At the bank we went through the drive-through. Then, at the post office, Mother went in and I stayed in the car with Tanisha. But at the grocery store we all went in. Twice while we were walking into the store, Tanisha walked behind a car that was backing up. If we wouldn't have grabbed her, she could have been run over." The chicken waterer was full, so Marilyn put the top on. The two girls walked toward the chicken house, carrying the waterer between them.

"What!" exclaimed Twila. "Even Robbie knows better than that!" She pulled open the door, and the two girls entered.

Chickens flapped their wings and cackled. Marilyn shooed them with her foot and set the waterer in its place. She continued with her story. "While we were in the store, she'd talk to anyone. You should have seen people smile at her and tell her what a cute little girl she was!" Marilyn scooped some laying mash from a barrel in the corner and dumped it into the feeder. Her voice was full of disgust.

Twila gathered another egg from a nest and rolled her eyes. "If they only knew!"

"We held her hand and tried to keep our eyes on her at all times," Marilyn went on. "But one time Mother and I turned away for just a moment to decide what kind of lettuce we wanted.

When we turned around, Tanisha was eating grapes just as fast as she could stuff them into her mouth."

"Oh, no!" Twila groaned.

"We found the store manager, and Mother apologized and paid for the stolen grapes. That's what made us late. The man was nice enough, but I'm sure he thought it was ridiculous that we couldn't control a four-year-old any better than that."

Twila shook her head. "What's wrong with her? It seems so strange that she would walk behind a moving car. And Robbie would never talk to total strangers, or at least not hold a conversation with them. Any child would be afraid to do that, but Tanisha doesn't seem to have a normal fear of strangers. Yet she's terrified of losing her next meal. It doesn't make sense!" Twila gathered the last egg, Marilyn secured the chicken house door, and the two girls headed for the house.

The rest of the family was just sitting down to eat. Marilyn and Twila quickly washed their hands and slid into their chairs at the table.

Twila felt almost sorry for Robbie that evening. He was in disgrace with the younger girls because they were certain he had destroyed her picture. Dad and Mother had apparently discussed it, because Robbie had been disciplined.

Twila went to bed that night feeling discouraged. She reached into the drawer of her nightstand and pulled out her journal and pen. For the next fifteen minutes she wrote rapidly, pouring out her frustrations and confusion over the incident of Robbie and her picture. She also wrote of Marilyn's account of Tanisha and their trip to town.

I wonder how I would act if I'd have been neglected like Tanisha, she wrote. *Why do I have it so good when other children out there have been through such terribly bad things?*

Marilyn poked her and asked sleepily, "Are you about done? I'd like to turn the light off."

"Just about," Twila murmured. She held her pen poised over the paper; then she wrote, *This may sound silly, but I'm scared of what Tanisha is going to do next.*

She shut her journal and slid it back into the drawer. She lay back against her pillow with a sigh. Maybe now she could relax and go to sleep.

But Twila's mind insisted on rehearsing the days and weeks since Tanisha had come. Her thoughts kept twisting back around, trying to come up with answers and solutions for Tanisha's problems, but it was impossible. She wanted to give it to God and find peace, as she had a few days ago. But Tanisha's latest behavior loomed huge in her mind. Would Dad and Mother know what to do for a child whose actions were so bewildering? Finally she nudged Marilyn with her elbow. "Do you feel like me?" Twila wondered.

"Hmm? How's that?" Marilyn asked sleepily.

"I feel like I'm falling into a deep black hole and I can't get out," Twila explained. "Sooner or later I won't even be able to see the light at the top anymore."

"I don't know as I feel like that," Marilyn answered. "But I know what you mean. Just try not to get too discouraged. I keep praying that Dad and Mother will know what to do for Tanisha."

"I've been praying too!" exclaimed Twila. "I don't think I've ever prayed so much in my life!"

"And God will hear our prayers," Marilyn said firmly. "I just read tonight in 1 Peter, 'The eyes of the Lord are over the righteous, and his ears are open unto their prayers.'⁴ We just have to keep trusting that God cares and that He'll answer according to His will."

_____

4 1 Peter 3:12

Marilyn sounded so confident that Twila found a measure of comfort in her words. She played the words of the verse over and over in her mind, and at last she was able to fall asleep.

Twila awoke the next morning to hear Marilyn stirring around the bedroom. She cracked her eyes open enough to see the alarm clock. It was still early. She was about to turn over and go back to sleep, but Marilyn's voice stopped her. "Better get up. Mr. and Mrs. Graham are coming today. Remember, Mr. Graham promised to help Dad install the new flooring."

Twila lay still, thinking about the day ahead. She thought of Tanisha and wondered how she would act. Would she charm the Grahams like she did everyone else outside the family? She remembered the conversation she and Marilyn had had the night before. She would try not to worry about Tanisha, but trust God and her parents to take care of her.

Twila jumped out of bed, threw on her clothes, and stood in front of the mirror to comb her hair. When she was finished, she joined her family for breakfast.

After breakfast Mother and the younger girls cleared the table and cleaned up the kitchen. Marilyn and Twila helped Dad move the table and chairs into the living room.

Robbie came running into the dining room, yelling, "Mr. Grams are here! Mr. Grams are here!"

Mr. and Mrs. Graham had come through the woods, with Mr. Graham walking and Mrs. Graham riding on her power-controlled wheelchair.

Dad went to the back door and welcomed them. He helped Mr. Graham get Mrs. Graham's chair into the house. She wheeled herself into the living room to watch everything that was going on. Mrs. Graham's face was animated as she spoke of the warm spring weather. "I never get tired of looking at the spring beauties!" she exclaimed. "They're so tiny and they have such a delicate beauty."

Dad and Mr. Graham went to work, tearing up the old flooring. The girls hauled it out and threw it in the trailer Dad had parked near the back door. After that, there wasn't much more the girls could do to help with the flooring. So they helped Mother in the kitchen and visited with Mrs. Graham.

Mother was making homemade rolls for the pork barbecue sandwiches she was planning to serve for lunch. She came to the door frequently to see how the work was progressing. There was a light in Mother's eyes that Twila hadn't seen for a while, as she expressed her pleasure in the new floor.

Robbie bounced around Mrs. Graham's chair, chattering and telling her stories. She responded in her usual gruff way, but Twila could see she liked the little fellow. However, Mrs. Graham didn't seem to be particularly taken with Tanisha, despite the little girl's efforts to get her attention.

Once, when Tanisha wanted to go outside, she came to Mrs. Graham and asked sweetly, "Could you please zip my jacket for me?"

But Mrs. Graham only sniffed and said, "Do it yourself. You're a big girl!"

About an hour later, Tanisha came back in. She kicked off her boots and dropped her jacket on the floor. She went into the living room and leaned on the arm of Mrs. Graham's chair. "I gave Robbie ten rides in the wagon and seven rides on the swing," she announced. "And then he fell down and bumped his knee so I helped him get up. His knee was bleeding, so I put a Band-Aid on it for him."

Mrs. Graham grunted. "Humph. I wonder what your mother would say if I asked her how you treat Robbie."

Tanisha's eyes flashed, and after that she avoided Mrs. Graham.

Twila could hardly believe the story about the hurt knee. She had been nearby all morning, and she hadn't seen Robbie or

Tanisha come in for a Band-Aid. She slipped out the back door to find Robbie playing on the trailer. "Hey, Robbie," she said. "How's your knee feeling?"

Robbie gave her an odd look. Twila pushed up first one of Robbie's pant legs and then the other. Both knees were in perfect health. Robbie pushed her away indignantly. "Nuffing wrong with my knees!"

Hmmm! Twila went back into the house.

By noon the linoleum was installed, except for putting the trim back in place. Dad, Mother, and the Grahams ate at the kitchen table with Robbie and Tanisha. The afternoon sun was so warm that the rest of the girls took their plates outside to eat.

A couple of hours later, the work was completed and the table and chairs were placed back in the dining room where they belonged. They all stood around and admired the finished results. Mother, especially, was pleased. "Thank you, Alex and Mr. Graham, for your hard work. The floor looks really nice!"

The Grahams went home, and Dad left with the truck and trailer to haul away the load of old flooring. The girls helped Mother clean up the house and get food ready for Sunday dinner.

After supper the younger children had been bathed and put to bed when the phone rang. Dad came out of the office and said, "Mary Ann, that was Carl Hoover. Their fridge stopped working, and so today they bought a new one. He's wondering if I'd come over and help him get it into the house. So I'm going to go over. It shouldn't take too long."

Twila was heading for bed when Mother remembered the greenhouse. "Twila, I want you to go out and water the plants. Close up the greenhouse too before you come in. It was warm today, but it's turned chilly this evening."

Slipping on her flip-flops, Twila ran out to do as she was told. A moment later she stood stunned at the doorway of the greenhouse. Such destruction she could never have imagined!

Mother's beautiful vegetable and flower plants were dumped in a heap. Flats and flower containers were scattered everywhere. Only two trays that apparently couldn't be reached were left untouched. The others were scattered on the floor. It looked as though someone had deliberately stomped over top of everything.

Fierce anger swept through Twila. Though she knew Tanisha would never admit it, there was no doubt in Twila's mind about who had done this. It had to be Tanisha. Nobody else in their family would do such a thing! It seemed whatever Mother enjoyed, Tanisha was determined to spoil. Only last evening Mother had commented on how nice and sturdy the plants in the greenhouse were. They would be the perfect size to set out in a few days if the weather stayed nice.

Several evenings before, Dad had plowed up another twenty feet on the end of the garden so they would have room for more plants. Would they even need it now, with all these plants ruined? All this flashed through Twila's mind as she stared dumbly at the wreckage.

Why? she wondered. *Why does Tanisha hate Mother so?*

With heavy feet, Twila walked back to the house to tell Mother. Just then Dad pulled in the driveway, so Twila waited on the sidewalk for him. She might as well tell Dad first. She wanted to put off telling Mother as long as possible. She couldn't bear the thought of the look on Mother's face when she saw what had happened.

Dad stared at the mess in dazed silence, then slowly shook his head. He sighed. "Tanisha must have done this while we were distracted with our work in the house today. I guess we'd better go get Mother. We'll have to see if we can salvage anything."

Dad, Mother, Marilyn, and Twila worked late into the night, sifting through dirt and carefully salvaging any plants that hadn't been snapped off or smashed beyond hope. What could be saved was discouragingly little. Nobody said much, but more than once Twila saw Mother wiping tears. She didn't blame her; she wanted to cry herself. They had put so many hours of work into the plants, only to have them destroyed. It was so senseless and wasteful!

Twila wondered dismally, *How can we keep living with a child who is so destructive? She seems to have no conscience!*

Finally, they were done. They stood looking at the pitifully few plants that had been repotted and placed back on the shelves. They looked sad and bedraggled.

"Well, I guess that takes care of that," Mother said with a sigh. "I was wondering how I could handle a produce garden when Tanisha takes so much of my time. But she nicely took care of the problem for us. Alex, do you think we could plant a good part of the garden back into grass again?" There was weariness in Mother's voice.

Dad placed an arm around Mother's shoulders. "Is that what you want, dear?" he asked softly.

Marilyn and Twila did not wait to hear her reply. They silently slipped away into the house.

CHAPTER SEVEN

A Child Who Has Never Been Loved

Twila pushed her pail farther down the corn row and reached for another handful of weeds. The June sunshine shone down like a warm blanket, and a gentle breeze played through her dark hair. It was a day that should have made one feel glad to be alive. But Twila felt a weariness that pierced all the way through her.

She straightened to relieve the ache in her back. Her eyes drifted to the sad-looking tomatoes they had planted next to the corn patch. Farther over were the broccoli, cauliflower, and brussels sprouts. These vegetables and a few flowers were all they had been able to save from the destruction Tanisha had caused in the greenhouse.

Mother had a way with plants, and Twila could not remember a year when their garden had looked this bedraggled—or weedy, for that matter. Mother had always loved to garden and had some-how managed to get the rest of the family enthused about it too. But this year, strangely, Mother didn't seem to care.

Twila and Marilyn had entertained high hopes that once they were home from school to help Mother with the work, life with Tanisha would go better. Instead, Twila felt as if a tidal wave had washed over her. She had known before how frustrating Tanisha was, but she had been in school every weekday. Now that she was home all day, every day, there was no escaping Tanisha's difficult behavior.

Daily it seemed that Tanisha grew worse and her conduct more puzzling. Robbie refused to play with her. If the two happened to be alone for even a moment, he inevitably came away crying. Mother and the older girls could never really discover what happened. The three middle girls avoided being around Tanisha as well. Robbie's occasional nightmares had increased. Now almost every night he woke the rest of the family with his terrified screams.

One day Tanisha gashed her foot while playing outside. She came in at lunchtime and was about to sit up to the table when Rita cried out, "Mother, look! Tanisha's bleeding!"

A trail of blood led all the way from the outside door to the table. As Tanisha sat in her chair, looking unconcerned, blood dripped from her foot. Mother took charge. "Quick, Twila, bring me a clean rag. Suzanne, run and get a stainless steel bowl with warm water. Marilyn, go to the bathroom and bring me some salve, gauze, and tape."

Twila found a rag and rushed back to Mother. Mother took it and clamped it over the wound. When the bleeding slowed, she gently washed Tanisha's small foot in the bowl of water Suzanne had brought.

"She's got an owie," said Robbie solemnly. "A really bad one!"

"Poor Tanisha," said Rita sympathetically. "Doesn't it hurt?"

Tanisha looked up blankly at Rita. "No," she said simply.

Mother applied a generous amount of salve to a piece of gauze. She gently pressed it against the wound and taped it on. "The cut is fairly deep, but not as bad as I first thought."

Now Twila stared at the patch of dirt in front of her and pondered the incident. *Why didn't Tanisha admit that her foot hurt? It had to have hurt! Has Tanisha experienced so many painful things that she no longer feels pain?* She didn't understand.

And the lying! Twila had never seen a child who lied like Tanisha. She lied for no reason. She lied when it wasn't even to her benefit to lie. In fact, almost everything Tanisha said was a lie!

On June 10, Tanisha had her fifth birthday, and the whole family had gone out of their way to make the day special for her.

The girls and Robbie had a lot of fun picking out a cute china tea set for Tanisha at the store. They were planning to give it to Tanisha after Dad came home from work. But Robbie and Rita were so excited to give it to Tanisha that Mother said she could open the package the morning of her birthday instead of waiting till evening.

Rita was eager to try out the dishes with Tanisha. "Come, Tanisha, let's set up our little table and chairs and ask Mother for some food so we can have a tea party!" But Tanisha didn't seem excited about the tea set, and she wouldn't help. Rita ended up doing most of the work herself. Robbie sat down to eat with them, and even then Tanisha would not cooperate. She grabbed a fistful of raisins from the little dish and stuffed them all into her mouth at once. She clinked her dishes and broke two of them.

"No, Tanisha! Be careful," pleaded Rita. "You're breaking them. And we want to share the food, not eat it all at once."

Tanisha only laughed and picked up the dainty little pitcher and drank all the lemonade in one big gulp. She plunked the pitcher down, and when the handle broke off in her hand, she laughed again.

Rita burst into tears. "Mother," she cried, "can't you please stop Tanisha? She's going to break all the dishes!"

They invited Grandma and Uncle Jerry's family to come in the evening to help celebrate Tanisha's birthday. Before they came, Tanisha had ruined the frosting on the dolly cake that Mother had decorated for her. "I don't like that old cake, and I don't want to have a party!" she yelled. But when the visitors arrived, she took Grandma's hand and exclaimed, "Thank you so much for coming for my birthday! I couldn't wait for you to get here!"

When it was time to eat the cake, Mother went to the kitchen to get matches to light the candles. While she was getting dessert plates and a knife to cut the cake, Grandma, Aunt Julia, and the children stood around the dining room table, admiring Tanisha's cute dolly cake. Ricky stopped short suddenly. Pointing at the smeared frosting, he said, "Hey, why is the frosting all ugly on this one side?"

"Robbie messed it up," said Tanisha.

Connie exclaimed, "Robbie did not do it. You did it!"

"No, I didn't," Tanisha insisted. "Robbie wrecked my cake!"

"But you know you did it!" exclaimed Rita.

Suzanne's eyes flashed. "There you go again, blaming Robbie for your sins and iniquities!"

Tanisha's pretty little face crumpled, and she started crying. "Everybody blames everything on me! Nobody likes me!" she said piteously.

Grandma looked distressed and opened her mouth to say something. But just then Mother entered the room with the plates and matches, and Dad and Uncle Jerry came in from the living room. Tanisha's face cleared instantly, and her tears disappeared.

"Here, Tanisha," said Mother. "Do you want to help me put the candles on your cake? We need five candles because you're five years old! You're getting to be a big girl, aren't you?" She smiled warmly at Tanisha.

Dad said heartily, "Well, why don't we sing for our birthday girl?"

Tanisha sidled up to Dad and held his hand. She smiled sweetly as everyone sang to her, but Twila noticed that when it came time to sing, "Happy birthday, dear Tanisha," Suzanne pinched her mouth shut and would not sing anymore.

Uncle Jerry and Aunt Julia gave Tanisha a doll's bottle that looked like it had real milk in it. Grandma gave her a coloring book and a box of crayons. Dad and Mother gave her a little brown baby doll with soft, fuzzy hair.

"Thank you, thank you!" Tanisha shouted after opening each gift and running to hug the givers. But after the birthday company had gone, she put the doll under her bed and refused to play with it.

Twila reached down and pulled another weed. Did Tanisha really not like her doll? But she must like it, because one day Twila had gone to Tanisha's room to get her dirty clothes for washing, and had found her playing with the doll.

Suddenly, Twila had to smile as the memories of Tanisha's birthday faded and the stamp episode flashed through her mind. Tanisha had taken the new roll of postage stamps Dad had bought for Mother and peeled them off and stuck them all over herself. She was a comical sight with stickers plastered on her cheeks and forehead. She had even stuck a stamp on the tip of her nose. More stamps marched in crooked rows up and down her arms.

Twila had been sure that Mother would be upset, but she only chuckled and said, "So, you like stickers? I don't blame you. I liked stickers too when I was a little girl."

Mother salvaged as many of the stamps as she could. Then she went to her room and pulled out a sheet of teddy bear stickers. She gave them to Tanisha, saying, "You may not play with stamps, but you may have these stickers." Though it was naughty of Tanisha to waste all those stamps, the happening would have been cute if it would have stopped there. But it didn't.

Rita looked wistfully at the sheet of cute little teddy bear stickers. "Mother, could I have some stickers too?"

"No," said Tanisha quickly. "You can't have any. Just me can have some!"

Mother reached out and smoothed back Rita's curly hair. "I do have one more sheet of stickers. They're not quite so nice; they're just smiley faces. But if you want them, you may have them."

When Tanisha saw Mother go to her room to get the stickers for Rita, she took her bear stickers behind the couch and tore them into tiny pieces. When Rita discovered her there amid the pieces, she was stricken. She could hardly bear to see those cute teddy bear stickers so deliberately ruined! But Tanisha only laughed and ran outside while Rita went to tell Mother.

Suzanne remarked bitingly to Twila, "I'd like to stuff that child in the mailbox, stamps and all, shut the door, put the flag up, and mail her right back to where she came from!"

Twila giggled, remembering Suzanne's comment, but her smile quickly faded. The incident wasn't really funny. What possessed Tanisha to act the way she did?

And then, not to be forgotten, were the strange nicks on the new dining room floor. They looked like they had been made with a knife. At first there had been many indignant exclamations, until it slowly dawned on them that here again, Tanisha must be responsible.

"I know it had to be Tanisha!" Suzanne exclaimed.

"We've never seen her do it, so we shouldn't accuse her of it if we don't know for sure," Marilyn cautioned.

"Had to be her," Suzanne said bluntly. "None of the rest of us would have done it. We never had this kind of funny stuff happen around here before she came."

"Well, Tanisha *said* she didn't do it," offered Twila.

Suzanne snorted. "Like that's any kind of proof. You can't believe a word she says."

It was true that Tanisha denied making the nicks in the linoleum, and no one ever saw her doing it. So if she had done it, it seemed the only time it could have happened was at night when the rest of them were all sleeping.

The mystery of it all gave Twila a sense of dread and waiting. If a five-year-old could sneak out of bed in the middle of the night and slip past Dad and Mother's bedroom without them hearing her, what would she try next?

Suddenly the tears began to slide down Twila's cheeks. They had all tried so hard to love Tanisha and forgive her for the awful things she did. They tried to show compassion and understand the reasons for her crazy behavior. But all Tanisha seemed to do was retaliate with behavior more terrible than before.

After school let out, Mother had decided that the family needed to eat more healthfully. They would eat desserts only on special occasions. In its place they would have more fruits and vegetables.

Twila noticed the changes and asked Mother one day, "How come you hardly let us girls do any baking anymore?"

"I'm hoping maybe some changes in diet will improve Tanisha's behavior. Certain foods can hinder our ability to function as well as we should in daily life. And it definitely doesn't hurt any of us to eat less sugar."

During strawberry season, however, Mother had surprised the family with a fresh strawberry pie for dessert one evening. With kindness and love, Mother had placed a piece of pie in front of each person. But Tanisha had turned her face away and refused to eat her piece.

Almost all of Tanisha's obstinacy seemed to be targeted at the things Mother enjoyed or had done for her. Worse than all the destruction was her unrelenting rejection of Mother. With unyielding stubbornness, she resisted the very smallest of Mother's instructions.

The first day Tanisha had arrived in their home, Rita had showed her how to set the table. Tanisha had set the table carefully and precisely that day, but now she pretended she didn't know how. She would put on big serving spoons instead of regular spoons, then act surprised when Mother corrected her. Another time she would put on the right spoons, but neglect to put on the forks. When confronted, she would open her eyes wide and exclaim, "Oh, I forgot!" And then the next time she would give everyone coffee mugs instead of the cups they usually used.

Twila pushed a strand of dark hair back from her face and reached for another weed. It was endless, really, what all Tanisha could imagine to do wrong. Just when you were sure there was no wrong way left to try, she would think of another one.

Whenever the family planned to go anywhere, it seemed Tanisha always spoiled their plans. She managed in some way to make them late or not go at all. No matter what the Hammonds planned, Tanisha seemed to take control of family happenings. She might "accidentally" shove Robbie into a mud puddle, and his clothes would have to be changed. Or she would spill something on her own clothes and then when she was instructed to go change, she would move with maddening slowness. This was a trial for everyone. Dad had taught them the importance of being on time, but Tanisha was making that almost impossible.

But she's only five! Twila told herself, feeling guilty for her mental accusations. *Are we being too hard on her? But no,* she thought, shaking her head. *It happens so often, she must be doing it on purpose!*

Worst of all, Dad seemed oblivious to the severity of the problem. He knew, of course, about Tanisha's worst behavior, but he didn't seem to comprehend the persistent rebellion that went on day after day. He saw only the loving little girl who flew into his arms every evening after work.

Twila felt guilty for resenting Dad's lack of discernment, and she was angry with Tanisha for causing her to feel this way about the dad she loved.

How could one little girl cause so much friction in a family? Tanisha did, and she did it well. Twila had only to look around to see the effects on each of her family members.

Mother was tired and exhausted—partly from continually working with Tanisha, and partly because she didn't sleep well at night for fear of what Tanisha would do while everyone else was sleeping.

Robbie was whiny and clingy. Rita, who never talked much, was quieter than ever. She spent hours swinging or sitting on the back step, holding her cat Patrick. Silently she would stroke his fluffy black and white fur over and over again.

Connie cried easily, and Suzanne turned more irritable than usual. She teased and played tricks and pranks, which only caused Connie to shed more tears.

Marilyn fled to the Grahams' every chance she got. Twila had never wanted to work for the Grahams before, but now she was envious of Marilyn's escape, and that made her feel even guiltier.

With the back of her hand, Twila wiped the perspiration from her forehead. Resentment, anger, and jealousy twisted inside her with overwhelming intensity. As a Christian, she knew it was wrong to feel this way, but she felt powerless to stop the feelings. She couldn't go to Mother; she was too preoccupied with Tanisha, and Twila didn't want to bother her with any more troubles. Dad didn't seem to understand. Twila didn't even try to talk about Tanisha to her friends at church. Everything was just too mixed up and crazy. Her friends would never understand or believe her if she tried to explain what was happening in their home.

Sometimes she and Marilyn talked. "Where is God? Can't He see what's happening?" Twila had asked Marilyn one day in desperation.

"He is there; we just need to keep praying," Marilyn tried to comfort.

"But I can't even think to pray anymore," Twila despaired. "My mind is so foggy and confused that about all I can say is, 'God! Please help!'"

The worse things became, the more it seemed liked the family was drifting into separate islands of their own. Twila felt hopeless and lonely.

And then yesterday, on top of everything else, there were the books. Twila still felt hurt and bewildered. She gave a hard jerk on a stubborn root as the scene of the day before flashed through her mind. Fresh tears stung her eyes and blurred her vision.

Twila had been browsing through the books in Dad's study and found two books she thought looked interesting. All the books in Dad's study had to be approved by Mother or Dad before the children could read them. So, hoping she was old enough to read the two books she had selected, she took them to Mother to ask her permission.

"Mother, would it be okay if I read these books?" she asked.

Mother had just sat down to read to the younger children. But she took the books and paged through them. Tanisha and Robbie waited quietly while she checked them over.

Mother regarded the covers thoughtfully before saying, "This one is a doctrinal book of Dad's. I don't mind if you read it, but I think it will be a bit above your head. This other book is an autobiography of the author's life, starting from before he was a Christian. It gives plenty of exposure to what happens out in the world. While it's realistic and true of how ungodly people live their lives, I really don't want you to be introduced to those kinds of lifestyles at your age. In this world we live in, you will get exposed soon enough."

Twila put the autobiography back in the study. Although she was a little disappointed, she wasn't surprised at what Mother had said. But she had been hoping for something new to read. She had already read all the books in the living room bookcase. She took the other book and sat down on the couch and tried to read it. She soon gave up though, because Mother was right. It was above her head, and she could hardly understand any of it. She put that book away too, and then wandered outside to find something else to do.

Later that afternoon, Mother had gone into Marilyn and Twila's bedroom to take the sheets off the bed. By now, Twila was back in the house writing a letter at the dining room table. She was just signing her name when Mother entered the room with the forbidden book. There was disappointment in her voice as she spoke. "Twila, I found this book under your pillow when I pulled the sheets off your bed to wash them. I told you I didn't want you to read this book."

Twila looked in surprise at the book in Mother's hand. "But I put it back where I found it. I never even started reading it."

Mother looked puzzled. "But it was right there under your pillow. How did it get there if you didn't put it there? I don't understand."

Bewildered, Twila opened her mouth to speak, but Robbie was crying in the living room and Rita was calling for Mother.

"We'll need to talk about this with Dad when he comes home tonight," Mother said with a sigh as she turned to go see what was wrong with Robbie. So the subject was dropped until Dad came home.

Twila's pail was full, so she emptied the weeds on the pile, then came back to start her next row.

Though Twila was puzzled as to how the book had gotten under her pillow, she knew she hadn't put it there. The whole incident had slipped from her mind until after supper when Dad and Mother called her into the study to talk to her.

When Dad asked her what happened, Twila said she didn't know. But she tried to explain what she knew of the incident. "I put the book away in the study when Mother said I couldn't read it, but then all of a sudden, it was under my pillow." The explanation sounded flimsy, even to her own ears.

The more she hesitated, trying to answer Dad's questions, the more Dad and Mother seemed to question her sincerity. The realization that they doubted she was telling the truth, on top of the stress and difficulty of the last few months, made the confusion in her mind grow worse. Her words came out as jumbled and befuddled as she felt.

Twila could understand her parents' misunderstanding. After all, a book couldn't just grow legs and crawl under a pillow to hide! She was mystified herself. She almost wished that she had actually been guilty of sneaking the book so she could confess what she had done and take the consequences. Finally she gave up defending herself and was quiet.

Dad sighed. "Twila, I don't know what to say. It's not like you to be deceitful. We've always trusted you to tell the truth." He looked at Mother and then back to Twila again. "Since we just don't really know for sure what happened, we'll have to let this drop for now."

Mother sighed, and Twila sat before her parents, silently wiping her tears. How could Mother and Dad doubt her honesty in this situation? But even as she felt the unjustness of the situation, Twila felt sorry for Mother. She had been so tired and distracted lately, with Tanisha's problems towering over her.

Tanisha! Was she behind this incident too? But what reason would Tanisha have had to get the book out of the study and hide it there? She couldn't even read and hardly understood Mother's objection to Twila reading the book. How could it possibly have been Tanisha? It certainly wasn't fair to blame her for every little occurrence around the place. Thinking about it again, Twila was just as confused as she had been yesterday. The tears spilled over once more.

When Twila had finished weeding her designated four rows of corn, she didn't stop. She had no desire to step back into the endless friction in the house. She worked steadily on until she had finished the last corn row. As she dumped her pail of weeds, she heard Connie calling from the house to come in for lunch.

The afternoon was long and difficult. In spite of their efforts to keep an eye on Tanisha, she managed to sneak a pair of scissors and cut the hair off the cat. On his back leg was a nasty cut. Tanisha declared she hadn't meant to hurt Patrick, but no one paid much attention to what she said.

Rita's beloved Patrick was a hideous sight. Even the hair of his tail had been trimmed. There were a few patches that had been missed, so after doctoring the cut, Mother tried to trim the rest of his hair. But Patrick, tired of the tender mercies of humans, squirmed away and refused to allow anything more to be done.

He did, however, allow Rita to hold him later. She was heartbroken. She sat on the back steps with tears trickling down her cheeks as she stroked again and again the scruffy hair of her cat. Twila wondered if she was crying over the cat or the conflict in their home. Maybe it was both.

Connie whimpered to Mother, "Tanisha is just so mean! I don't think I can take it anymore!"

Mother hugged the little girl against her and wordlessly patted her back.

Twila knew what Connie meant. She didn't think she could handle much more either. It seemed like every day they were thrown from one crisis to the next.

By the time Dad came home that evening, all of their nerves were at the breaking point. When Tanisha ran to Dad shrieking, "Daddy, Daddy!" Marilyn burst into tears and disappeared out the back door. Seeing Marilyn cry, Connie promptly started crying too. Twila swallowed hard and determined not to join them. She was afraid if she got started, she'd never be able to stop.

They all sat down to a silent supper table. Even Mother said nothing. In spite of her weariness, Mother had always before asked Dad about his day. But tonight she didn't seem to have the energy to say anything. Rita pushed her food around but didn't eat much. Suzanne grimly devoured her plate of food without looking up. Connie didn't even pretend to eat, but kept sniffing until Twila thought she would go crazy.

Only Tanisha chattered cheerfully to Dad. "I rode my trike today. I can ride it faster than Robbie. Robbie tipped over on his trike so I helped him get up. I played with Patrick. I petted him and Patrick likes me. He likes me better than Rita. I helped Twila in the garden. I pulled a whole bucketful of weeds!"

"Oh, did you?" For once, Dad's responses to Tanisha's chatter sounded absent and preoccupied.

As soon as they were done eating, the family scattered from the table. Only Dad stayed to help Mother with the dishes. Twila had a hunch that Marilyn was back in the woods at the rock where she liked to be alone. She headed out to find her.

Marilyn smiled wanly when Twila walked up. "I suppose you think I'm a big baby, but I just couldn't take it one minute more. Tanisha was *awful* today! And then when Dad came home, she was instantly all sweet and nice. I felt like I just had to get away from everything!"

Twila didn't answer. She sat down on the ground, leaned her back against the rock, and let the tears slide down her cheeks.

After a moment, Marilyn went on thoughtfully, "I know it's not fair to blame Dad or expect him to see what she's really like. She acts so differently when he's around. But I wish he could realize how she acts when he's not home! I wish he'd drop in unexpectedly someday and catch Tanisha right in the middle of one of her times when she's defying Mother. I've never seen a child who can play a double role like she does. She's so convincing, it's no wonder Dad doesn't understand."

Twila glanced up at Marilyn, feeling relief. "So you're having a hard time not being mad at Dad too?"

Marilyn nodded tearfully. "It's hard not to be upset at Dad, but it's mostly Tanisha I have a hard time loving and forgiving. She has come in and ruined our family life. We used to have so much fun, and it was peaceful to be together. Now we're all tired and upset with each other most of the time. It seems like I'm always angry, and I don't want to be that way. And . . ." Marilyn's words trailed off as fresh tears trickled down her cheeks.

The two girls sat together, silently wiping their eyes. There didn't seem to be much to say. It all seemed hopeless.

"You know," Marilyn went on, "when we had a little stillborn brother, it was hard, but we at least had the comfort of knowing he was in Heaven. But with Tanisha, there doesn't seem to be any comfort or hope in anything. I don't think anything could make Tanisha change. It seems Mother has tried everything short of spanking her, which of course she's not allowed to do to a foster child. No amount of coaxing or reasoning seem to help Tanisha in the least. To her, every rule is meant to be broken or misused in some way. And any love and compassion we show her is promptly thrown back in our faces. It's hard to believe she's not doing all these things on purpose. But it's almost like she has no idea why she's doing crazy things. She seems to act on impulse, without any reason at all."

Twila suddenly stiffened as she noticed Dad's tall figure strolling through the woods. He was obviously looking for them, because when he saw them, he turned and came down the trail that led to Marilyn's rock.

Dad said nothing at first, but squatted on the ground and leaned his back against a nearby tree. He picked up a leaf and tore it into little pieces.

Finally he looked up at his two oldest daughters. "Mother and I have been talking. I asked her to explain again to me what is going on with Tanisha and why everyone is so upset. I know Tanisha has been stubborn and defiant. But I'm gone during the day, and I seem to be missing some things."

Dad picked up a stick and absently scraped a patch of ground clear of leaves. "I think after talking to Mother this time, I'm finally beginning to understand. But I want to hear your side of the story. I want to know how *you* see things."

Sensing Dad's genuine desire to know, the girls hesitantly started talking. Dad kept asking questions, and the girls explained what they meant.

"The stuff she wrecks is bad enough," said Twila, "but the way she treats Mother is worse. It seems she blames Mother for all the bad things that ever happened to her, and she's determined to make Mother pay for it."

Marilyn added, "It's so hard to understand. It feels as if she must deliberately think through her desire to hurt Mother. A lot of the time, things happen so quickly that she's obviously not thinking, but is just reacting to her first impulse. If Mother is kind to her, Tanisha immediately does something negative back for no good reason. I don't believe she really thinks; it's just an automatic response."

"It's so strange, Dad!" Twila said. "All the foster children we've ever had before loved Mother. But Tanisha seems to hate her. She destroys everything that Mother enjoys. And when Mother does something nice for her, she just retaliates with more awful behavior. She's really good at keeping things in a perpetual turmoil!"

"And she's horribly sneaky, Dad!" said Marilyn. "We never quite know for sure what happened or who did it. Things disappear, and we don't know where they've gone. We almost never catch her in the act, and yet all these strange things happen. Everyone is suspicious of everyone else. We never had these kinds of problems before Tanisha came. Not like this! Sometimes when I do catch her in the very act of doing something naughty, she looks me straight in the eye and says she didn't do it. She's so convincing that I wonder if I'm crazy."

Dad sighed. "I'm sorry, girls. I feel like I've failed all of you. I should have seen the way things were sooner, but I didn't."

Twila's frustration with Dad suddenly began to melt away.

Marilyn exclaimed, "But, Dad, how could you know? How could you see the way things were when Tanisha is so convincingly two-sided? There's got to be something wrong with her! It feels like she spends all her time trying to divide our family."

"I guess that's what it's coming down to," said Dad. "Something is wrong with Tanisha. But what?"

"Mrs. Gunther talked about reactive attachment disorder. Is that what's wrong with her?" wondered Marilyn.

Dad nodded. "Mother and I are pretty sure she has some kind of developmental disorder, but we've never faced this kind of behavior in any of the other children we've fostered. So we don't know much about it."

Silence settled around them as the seriousness of the situation fell over them. They had in their home a child who had never been loved and who had no idea how to give and receive affection.

At last Dad spoke again. "Tell me, girls. Is it too much? We're still only fostering Tanisha. We have signed no papers committing ourselves to adoption. Do you think having Tanisha in our home is more than you or the rest of the family can handle?"

Twila pondered Dad's question. Dad's understanding had suddenly opened the doors of compassion in her heart again. If they all worked together, and with God's help, couldn't they try once more to reach Tanisha's heart?

Finally Twila spoke. "But, Dad, who will love Tanisha if we give up on her? Who will show her God's love if we don't? What would happen to Tanisha and all the other children like her if everyone would say it's not worth helping them?"

Tears shone in Dad's eyes, and his voice was husky. "Those are good questions, Twila. If we don't, who will? But the question also is, what is God's will for *our* family? And what about your little brother and sisters? They still need a lot of time and attention from Mother and me also. We want to follow His leading. Wherever God takes us, He will give us the strength we need."

For a moment there was silence. Then Dad said, "Why don't we pray before we go back to the house?"

Father and daughters bowed their heads, and in the stillness of the woods, Dad brought the matter before the Lord. As he prayed, tears slid down Twila's cheeks. They were no longer tears of hurt and confusion, but of renewed hope. A gentle peace spread over her soul. She felt fresh courage to go on.

She wiped the tears with the back of her hand and listened closely. "We thank You, heavenly Father, that You love us and care about us. We thank You that You know our needs and that we can call upon You in times of trouble. We ask You to guide us in this situation with Tanisha. We pray for direction. We pray for wisdom. We don't know which way to turn, but we want to surrender it all to You. We thank You for the knowledge that You have the answers, and we want to trust You for them. I thank You for each one of my children. I want to pray especially for Marilyn and Twila. May Your blessing rest upon them as they live for You. May our time of sharing together draw us closer to one another, and may there be a healing of relationships in our family. Bless each one and help us to walk in Your ways. In Jesus' name. Amen."

A feeling of closeness and understanding hung between them as Dad and the girls walked the woods trail back to the house in the dusky twilight.

CHAPTER EIGHT

A Glimmer of Hope

Amid all the turmoil over Tanisha, the Hammonds received a call that Mother's elderly aunt had passed away. Although Aunt Grace had suffered from Alzheimer's for years, her death was still something of a shock. Hasty plans were made for travel to the funeral, which would be seven hours' drive away.

Dad wasn't able to take off work, so it was decided that Mother, Twila, and Tanisha would go. Grandma Hammond and Aunt Grace had known each other as girls. So Grandma Hammond also wanted to go along. Marilyn would stay at home and keep house for Dad and the younger children.

Thursday morning at five o'clock found Grandma, Mother, Twila, and Tanisha traveling through the semidarkness. They had planned to leave early enough so they could arrive at their destination in plenty of time for Grandma to have a rest before going to the viewing that evening.

Twila leaned back in her seat and relaxed. After the stress of the last few weeks, it felt good to just sit back and do nothing. The sunrise was beautiful, and Twila thought she ought to get up early more often to see the sun come up. She wasn't like Dad and Marilyn, who bounced out of bed early every morning.

The miles slipped away as Grandma and Mother talked about flowers, gardens, and family. "You know how worried I was about Jerry's twins," Grandma said. "Well, they're finally starting to say words now. Janice is getting to be a real little chatterbox. I can't understand much of what she says though. Justin doesn't say a lot, but what he does say is easier to understand. I don't know why I ever waste my time worrying. You'd think at my age I'd know enough to leave things in the hands of the Lord and the younger generation."

"I don't suppose worrying ever did anyone any good," Mother replied. "But don't stop praying or being concerned for your children and grandchildren. We need it!"

Grandma looked keenly at Mother. "These last few months have been difficult for you, haven't they?"

"Yes," Mother said simply.

Twila looked over at Tanisha to see if she was listening. If she was, she gave no sign.

Grandma adjusted her seat belt. "I can't say I understand what you're going through, but how well I remember those first few months after Jerry brought Ricky home. He was unlike any child I had ever seen. Jerry and I were so confused and frustrated. Once he was diagnosed with an attention disorder, it wasn't so hard because we had some explanation for the brain functions that made his behavior so frustrating. It was not knowing that was so difficult."

"Alex and I have been doing a lot of praying about that very thing," Mother responded. "We feel like it's time to find out what exactly we're dealing with. We were planning to meet with our caseworker this week and see what recommendations she would have for us. But now with Aunt Grace passing away, we had to put it off until I get back."

Grandma reached up to pull the sun visor down to block the sun shining in her eyes. "I want you to know I *have* been praying for you. And now that I know you're searching for help, I'll pray that God will lead you to the right people."

It had been full daylight for a couple of hours, and the travelers were getting hungry and ready for a chance to get out and stretch. Mother found a restaurant that served a breakfast buffet, and they stopped to eat.

Tanisha got out of the car chattering. "I'm hungry, Grandma. Are you hungry? I'm going to eat lots of food. May I hold your hand? I like holding your hand. You're my favorite Grandma!"

They walked into the restaurant with Tanisha holding Grandma's hand. After the waitress showed them to a table, they bowed their heads and prayed before going through the line. Tanisha went with Grandma, and she helped Tanisha find a plate and fill it.

"You know," said Grandma to Mother when they returned to the table, "Tanisha picked out all the food she knows you want her to eat. She picked out mostly fruit and yogurt." Grandma smiled approvingly at Tanisha.

Twila felt anger rise within her as Tanisha shot Mother a smug look. *Tanisha has no desire to please Mother,* she thought. *She chose the food she did because she wants Grandma to think she's a sweet, obedient little girl. She wants Grandma to think Mother is too strict with her.*

Twila sighed. It was so frustrating! She felt quite sure Grandma had no idea how her comment would only make it more difficult for Tanisha to respect and appreciate Mother.

Aunt Grace's family had made arrangements for the Hammonds to stay with the William Bender family over the visitation and funeral. The Benders attended the same church Aunt Grace had attended.

When the Hammonds arrived at their destination several hours later, they were welcomed at the door by a pleasant-faced woman with graying hair. Standing beside her were two children with dark eyes and hair much like Robbie's and Connie's.

"Hello! I'm glad you made it here safely," she said warmly. "I'm Rachel Bender. And this is Luis and Raquel." Her hands rested lightly on the children's shoulders as she spoke.

"Luis and Raquel, can you tell these ladies how old you are?" Rachel prompted.

"I'm five," Luis responded with a big grin. Raquel shyly held up four fingers.

"I'm five too!" said Tanisha. "I just had my birthday." Rachel smiled her acknowledgment, and Luis beamed broadly.

"Come on in and make yourselves at home," said Rachel. Grandma went to lie down for a nap, and after allowing Tanisha some time to play, Mother took her and also went to rest for a while.

Twila had slept in the van, so she didn't feel at all tired. Looking out the window, she saw a girl hard at work in the garden picking peas. Somewhat hesitantly she asked Rachel if it would be all right if she went out and helped her.

Rachel chuckled. "I'm sure she'd be happy to have your help. But you don't need to feel obligated to do our work!"

Twila slipped out the back door and walked to the garden. The girl in the garden straightened and smiled a welcome when she saw Twila.

"Hi! My name is Jill. I saw your car drive in the lane, and I was itching to come in and meet you. But I was afraid if I stopped, I wouldn't get this last row of peas picked before the viewing tonight. And I've been working out here for hours!"

Twila felt herself instantly warming to Jill's cheerful greeting. She replied, "Well, my name is Twila, and if you don't mind,

I'll help you pick. Then you won't have to spend quite so many hours out here."

Jill laughed. "It's not that bad, really. But you know how it is when you work in the garden and you're hot and dirty. You feel like you'll never get done!"

Twila took the empty pail Jill offered and bent down to pick the fat pods that were hanging thickly on the pea vines. They soon discovered that Jill was several years older than Twila, but the two girls continued to chat comfortably.

With two of them picking peas, the girls were done in short order. Each lugging a pail, they went to the back porch and started shelling them. When Mother and Grandma were done napping, they came out and joined the girls.

As soon as they had enough shelled, Rachel took the peas into the kitchen to clean and blanch them for the freezer. When they were finished shelling the peas, Mother stood up and said, "If we're done here, I think I'm going to comb Tanisha's hair for tonight."

Rachel picked up the last bowl of peas and paused to look at Tanisha standing by Mother. She said to Mother, "What kind of hair products do you use for her? I have some leftover from a little girl we fostered a couple of years ago. You'd be welcome to use them."

Sensing that here was someone who understood African-American hair care, Mother plied Rachel with questions. "Would you mind showing me how to take care of Tanisha's hair? Her hair is getting so dry. I know I'm doing something wrong, but I don't know how to do it right."

"Sure, I'd be glad to show you what I've learned." Rachel glanced at the clock. "I think we have enough time that I could even comb Tanisha's hair in cornrows for you if you want me to."

"Yes, I would like that," said Mother. "Maybe if I watch you, I can learn to do the braiding myself."

"Oh, I'm sure you can do it," said Rachel as she pulled hair supplies from a cupboard. "It's not that hard once you learn how. It just takes time to make all the braids. But once you're done, you shouldn't have to do it again for several weeks."

Mother settled Tanisha into a chair and unbraided her two braids so Rachel could work. With deft fingers, Rachel carefully divided Tanisha's hair into many parts. As she combed, she explained the benefits of oils, creams, special brushes, and combs for different types of hair.

Twila watched in fascination as Rachel began braiding Tanisha's curly hair into smooth cornrows. An hour later, Tanisha had a whole new look. Twila was amazed. "It looks so nice!" she exclaimed. "Before, her hair was dry and frizzy-looking. Now it looks so neat and healthy!"

"Braiding curly hair in tight cornrows helps to keep the moisture in," Rachel responded. "That's why combing little African-American girls' hair in the traditional two braids doesn't work very well. It doesn't hold in the moisture. Tanisha's hair is still plenty dry, but if you keep her hair oiled like I showed you, Mary Ann, I think you'll soon see a difference.

"And here, you're welcome to keep these hair products," Rachel added as she screwed the lid on the last container. "I don't need them anymore. Have fun working with Tanisha's hair! It really is enjoyable once you get the hang of it. And it gives you lots of mother-daughter time."

Twila reached out and touched the box of beads lying on the table and asked, "What are these for?"

"Those can be attached to the bottom of the braids to hold them down," Rachel answered. Then, turning to Mother, she asked, "What do you think? Would you like me to put these on the ends of Tanisha's braids? As you notice, her braids are already starting to curl up. The beads weigh down the braids and keep them hanging straight."

Mother looked thoughtfully at the beads and then at Tanisha's hair. "Yes, I can see what you mean. Go ahead and put them in."

After Rachel showed her how, Mother helped her put them in. And then it was time for supper. They hurried to get the table set and the food on the table so they wouldn't be late for Aunt Grace's viewing that evening.

Throughout the two days with the Benders, Twila watched in fascination as Rachel Bender related to Luis and Raquel. She had never seen a parent who so closely supervised her children. Almost always, the children were right beside her, busily and happily engaged in some job or activity. If not right beside her, they were doing something quiet like coloring or playing with Lego blocks. With clear boundaries that Rachel strictly enforced, she took them through the day with such friendly guidance that the children were content and happy. When Rachel's husband William was around, he took over with gentle authority.

Twila felt wistful. Why couldn't her own family have this kind of peace and harmony? What was the secret to the Benders' success with their foster children?

What surprised Twila the most was that, unlike the church people at home, none of the Benders seemed to be taken in by Tanisha's superficial charm. Whenever Tanisha offered to help them set the table or some other job in the kitchen, both Rachel and Jill would firmly tell her that she must ask her mother first. And, though they were kind, they paid very little attention to Tanisha.

Twila observed that Tanisha seemed at first perplexed, and then angered by the way the Benders ignored her. She was not about to ask Mother for anything, so when her efforts to engage the Benders were rebuffed, she retreated into moody silence.

That first evening after they got home from the viewing, Rachel prepared a snack of sliced fruit, cheese, crackers, and tea for her guests. After they finished their snack, the three smaller children were tucked into bed. Grandma Hammond also retired for the night. But Mother, Rachel, and the two older girls lingered at the table, talking and enjoying another cup of tea.

Twila was beginning to feel the effects of a long day and listened drowsily as the two mothers visited.

"You mentioned that Tanisha came to you only recently through foster care," Rachel noted. "How is it going for you?"

Mother looked distressed and answered hesitantly. "I suppose it would look to most people as if it's going very well. When we're with people outside of our immediate family, Tanisha seems obedient and cooperative. At home we see another side of her. We've only done foster care for about two years, but Tanisha is the most challenging child we've faced yet. The way she acts at home and the way she behaves away from home are two entirely different things."

Mother gave her tea another stir. "I know you're a foster parent. Maybe you have some advice to give. Tanisha is very resistant to me. How do I know if the problem is with the child or with me? How does one know when it's the right time to reach out for professional help? Our caseworker has been telling us that she'll likely need therapy. We're having a meeting with her next week. We're planning to discuss some of these things, and she'll tell us what she and her supervisor decide."

Rachel poured herself some more tea before speaking. "William and I have been foster parents for over twenty years, and we've had many children in our home. Sometimes I think we've seen every type of behavior children can have, but whenever another child comes, we always learn something new.

"Out of all the children who have come through our home, we've adopted four. Our oldest son just got married six months ago. Our daughter Sara passed away at the age of eight from HIV and other health complications. And then there's Jill." Rachel paused to smile at her daughter. "After Jill comes our fifteen-year-old son, Thad."

The mention of Thad puzzled Twila. She hadn't seen a teenage boy since they had arrived at the Bender home. She popped a grape into her mouth and decided to ask Mother about it later.

"At the present, we have Luis and Raquel in our home as foster children," Rachel continued. "It appears they may soon be placed for adoption, and because they've lived with us for three years, we'll be given the first opportunity to adopt them."

Rachel looked at Mother. "But back to your question about Tanisha. With adoption there are always lots of questions and not always cut-and-dried answers. Keep asking questions. That's what all good parents do. I think maybe we adoptive parents just have a double portion of questions. But remember, we may ask for a double portion of God's Spirit and wisdom too!"

Rachel took another sip of her tea. Twila was wide awake now and listening closely to what Rachel had to say. Somehow, even though Rachel was talking to Mother, her understanding words were also a balm to Twila's troubled heart.

Rachel went on. "I'm not an expert. I'm just an adoptive mom who has a heart for adoption. And we definitely have made more than our share of mistakes in parenting. But I can tell you what I've learned from years of working with troubled children and what we observe about your child."

Rachel paused again as though reluctant to go on. "Observing Tanisha in just the short time you've been here, my husband and

I feel that you have a very emotionally disturbed child, primarily in issues of attachment. The problem is definitely not you!"

There it was again. Attachment disorder! Twila sank back in her chair and let the words sink in. Mother sat still and didn't speak for a long time. Finally she said slowly, "So, what's your advice for us?"

Rachel leaned forward and said earnestly, "In parenting a troubled child, accept your limitations. Reach out for godly resources. And don't overestimate your ability to make everything turn out right in the end. My husband and I have wished many times that we would have known more about attachment issues, especially as we raised our son Thad." Rachel's voice trembled, and she paused a bit before going on.

"We thought Thad was bonded to us as a child, but he had a way of retreating into an imaginary world. As he grew older, it came to the point where it seemed he was living in the blackness of sin and deceit. The more we tried to help him, the angrier he became, and our relationship deteriorated. Now he's in a boys' camp in another state."

Twila shifted in her chair. *So that's where Thad is.*

"If we had known when he was a small boy where this was leading, we would have tried much harder to find a way to help him. We've learned much through this painful experience. I'm telling you this so you can avoid the mistakes we've made."

Rachel poured more tea into Mother's cup, and the two continued sharing their experiences. What a blessing it was for Twila to see that, finally, Mother had a friend who really understood! Rachel thought there was hope for Tanisha, without blaming Mother for the problem.

"Pray for us, and pray for our son Thad," Rachel concluded as they rose from the table and cleared away their tea dishes. "We will certainly pray for you. We adoptive families need to be there for each other. I'm well aware of the maze you're navigating. The answers for your questions don't come easily. This is a time when your communication with God begins in earnest, and you realize you have to lean on Him for answers."

As they drove home after the funeral the next day, Twila stared out the window and pondered deep thoughts, questions, and ideas that were almost too hard for her young mind to grasp. And yet, for the first time, she felt hopeful about having Tanisha in their home. Rachel Bender had said that somewhere there were answers and people who could help. She prayed that Dad and Mother would know where to look.

CHAPTER NINE

I'm Just a Bad Girl

"Marilyn! Twila!" An insistent voice pulled Twila out of a deep sleep. She cracked open an eye to see Dad standing over them.

"Girls, I'd like you to get up and make breakfast so Mother can sleep a little longer. She didn't get much rest last night. She woke up in the middle of the night when she thought she heard a noise. We found Tanisha in her room playing with matches. Mother couldn't sleep after that."

The girls sat up, suddenly wide awake. Dad left the room, and the girls pulled themselves out of bed. When they got downstairs, Dad was finishing a bowl of cereal. "Was Tanisha actually playing with matches last night?" Twila was shocked.

Dad nodded and stood up, placing his spoon and bowl into the sink.

"What are we going to do?" Marilyn wailed. "It's not safe to go to sleep in our beds. She's going to burn the house down around us!"

Dad looked tired. "Mrs. Gunther told Mother that playing with matches and knives is not uncommon for children who come from hard situations. She also mentioned that there's an alarm system available that lets you know if a child leaves the room. We'll have to ask her more about it. Just pray about it, girls, and remember that God does have answers, even for children like Tanisha. It just takes wisdom to know how to find them," he encouraged.

Dad left the house to load some supplies onto the back of his truck while Twila quickly packed a lunch for him. When he came back in, she had it ready. "Have a good day!" he called over his shoulder as he went out the door.

Marilyn was making breakfast for the younger children, and Twila heard her mutter, "A good day? With Tanisha in the house?"

Dread rose within Twila. How could they get through another morning with Tanisha? How could they endure one more turbulent day? Her eyes caught sight of a song Mother had taped on the window above the kitchen sink only yesterday. She stood still and read down through the whole poem, and then she read the chorus twice:

"Got any rivers you think are uncrossable,
Got any mountains you can't tunnel through?
God specializes in things thought impossible,
He does the things others cannot do."[5]

Twila gave a deep sigh and squared her shoulders. Somehow this poem gave her courage for one more day. If there was ever an impossible situation, dealing with Tanisha certainly was! She turned to Marilyn to ask what she was supposed to do next.

They wakened the other children, and Twila and Marilyn tried to keep them as quiet as possible so Mother could sleep. The younger children looked sober and worried when Marilyn told them that Mother needed some more rest. But Tanisha laughed and cheered. She clattered around the house and made so much noise that Twila finally took her outside.

"Here, Tanisha!" said Twila. "Let me help you up on the swing." But Tanisha refused to get on.

"No, I want to run around the yard and make noise. I want to wake Mother up." Tanisha gave a nasty laugh. She ran loops around the yard, making all kinds of racket.

5 Copyright © 1945 New Spring Publishing Inc. (ASCAP) (adm. at CapitolCMGPublishing.com) All rights reserved. Used by permission.

Finally, Twila grabbed Tanisha as she ran past and said, "Let's go back to the woods and walk the trails." She felt desperate to get Tanisha away from the house so Mother could sleep. Tanisha hesitated and then, to Twila's surprise, followed her to the woods. Twila took the smaller girl's hand and Tanisha let it rest limply in hers.

Twila tried to point out things of interest, but the life had suddenly gone out of Tanisha, and she just stared with vacant eyes. Somehow it made Twila hurt just to look at that empty face. She thought she'd rather deal with a loud Tanisha than with this blank, silent one.

Twila said impulsively, "Tanisha, why do you do all this bad stuff? Why do you want to wake Mother? Why did you chop up the curtains and wreck those stickers Mother gave you?"

Tanisha looked back at her with hopeless eyes. She shrugged. "I'm just a bad girl. I'll never be good anyway. Nobody likes me!"

"But you're not bad," argued Twila. "You could be good if you tried. And we do love you!"

Tanisha shook her head despondently. "I'm just a bad girl. Nobody can love someone as bad as me."

When they got back to the house, Mother was awake and Twila was glad to pass her responsibility back to Mother.

That afternoon Dad came home from work early. Mrs. Gunther came and had her scheduled meeting with Mother and Dad. While they talked, Marilyn and Twila went out to the yard and played a game of croquet with the younger girls. About an hour later they heard Mrs. Gunther's car leave. They finished the game of croquet, and then the two older girls went back into the house to see how the visit had gone. They found Mother in the kitchen preparing supper.

"Marilyn, why don't you get a head of lettuce out of the refrigerator and cut it up for a salad?" Mother directed. "There should be some broccoli, cauliflower, and tomatoes in the bottom drawer as well. Twila, you may get a loaf of banana bread from the bread box and slice it." As she talked, she diced up some onions to be cooked with the liver she was frying.

Marilyn pulled out a cutting board and began dicing salad ingredients. "So, did Mrs. Gunther have any advice?" she wondered.

Mother added onions to the meat and gave them a stir before answering. She looked up at Marilyn with a faint smile. "Mrs. Gunther wants us to take Tanisha to a therapist and have her evaluated. Dad told her we preferred to take Tanisha to a Christian therapist, and she was very respectful of our wishes. She said there's one on staff at the clinic, and she'll try to get an appointment for Tanisha with her. Mrs. Gunther was very understanding of the struggles we've been having. She had a lot of tips and advice for us. Dad and I felt very encouraged by our meeting with her."

"Well, maybe going to therapy will help Tanisha to feel better too," said Twila. "She told me today that she's just a bad girl and nobody loves her."

Mother looked up from the stove and asked, "What did you tell her?"

Twila shrugged. "I told her that she's not a bad girl and that we *do* love her."

Mother picked up a paring knife and cut through a chunk of liver in the frying pan to see if it was done. She turned back to Twila. "I know why you said that—it's the easy thing to say. But the next time she says she's too bad to love, tell her you're sorry she feels that way. Contradicting her could seem like you're dismissing her feelings and problems. I think she truly does feel like she's bad and worthless. She needs us to express compassion, not just brush her feelings away."

Twila's heart sank; she had messed up again. But Marilyn said thoughtfully, "So that's the way to handle that. I wondered! Tanisha has said similar things to me. I wasn't sure what to tell her."

Mother spooned the meat from the pan onto a platter. "Don't feel bad if you don't get it right the first time," said Mother. "We're all learning together. Whether it's relating to troubled children or some other relationship, we always have things to learn. That's just life."

Twila felt relieved to know she wasn't the only one who struggled to say the right thing. Supper was ready, and as Twila went to call everyone in, she felt optimistic again. Maybe a therapist would provide the answers Dad and Mother were looking for. And most of all, they had a heavenly Father to guide them and give them wisdom.

The family sat down to the table, and after prayer, Dad filled Robbie's plate. The small boy dug into his food with gusto.

Twila saw Suzanne's nose curl when the platter of liver reached her. She made no comment but dutifully took a small portion. Twila also took a small piece and passed it on. She kept an eye on Robbie as he ate one, and then two pieces of liver. He chewed a little slower as the third piece went into his mouth. Suddenly he laid down his fork and exclaimed, "This meat tastes dusty!"

The family laughed, and Suzanne remarked, "I'll definitely agree with him on that."

"I never thought of it before, but 'dusty' is a perfect description of liver," Twila added.

Dad reached over with his fork, speared Robbie's last piece of meat, and popped it into his own mouth. He winked at Robbie. "Liver is good," he said. Robbie grinned, happy to see his last piece of liver disappear.

That evening after supper, Mother bathed Tanisha and put her to bed. It was Robbie's turn for a bath when the phone rang and Mother answered it. Dad was walking through the kitchen as Mother hung up. "Who was that?" he asked.

"That was Aunt Julia," Mother said slowly. "She and Uncle Jerry have been talking. They are offering to babysit Tanisha for us tomorrow to give us a break. Uncle Jerry will be home to help. I told her I'd talk to you, and we'd get back with them."

Dad looked thoughtful and then said, "I think it sounds like a good idea. Jerry and Julia have been very understanding. They're aware of how important it is to keep a child like Tanisha supervised. I think we should take them up on their offer."

At Mother's nod of agreement, Dad reached for the phone to call Uncle Jerry. Before dialing, he looked around the circle at the girls and asked, "How about going to Copper Falls tomorrow? I don't have any work planned that can't wait until next week."

The girls were delighted with the idea, but Mother looked tired. Marilyn gaily took her by the arm and led her to a chair. "You sit right here and tell us what to do to get ready. *We* will do the work!" she said dramatically.

Dad grinned. "If you girls can have everything ready, we'll leave nice and early tomorrow morning." He left the room with the phone to talk to Uncle Jerry.

Suzanne got out a piece of paper and a pen. "I'll write a list of the food and anything else we need to take along. What do you think we should have for lunch, Mother?"

Robbie suddenly appeared in the doorway. "Hot dogs!" he shouted. Seeing Mother was busy on the phone, he had taken a bath and dressed himself. His pajama bottoms were on right, but his T-shirt was backward. His hair was poorly dried, and water dripped down his cheeks.

"Robbie!" exclaimed Mother. "Did you take a bath all by yourself? I was going to help you!"

"Yep, I took a bath all by myself and washed my hair too!" For a moment Robbie looked vastly pleased with himself. Then he remembered and asked again, "But, can we please have hot dogs?"

Mother smiled at Robbie. "You'd eat hot dogs every day if we let you, wouldn't you? I think we do have some hot dogs in the freezer. We could have hamburgers too. There should be a place at the park where we can grill. Rita, run down to the basement freezer and get out two packs of hot dogs and a package of hamburger."

Suzanne wrote "hot dogs" and "hamburgers" on her list, along with all the condiments. "Mother, do you think we'd have time to make potato salad? You know how Dad likes it."

"That's a good idea," Mother said. "Marilyn, why don't you put some potatoes and eggs on to boil right now? Tomorrow on the way, we can stop somewhere and buy hot dog and hamburger buns, baked beans, and maybe a watermelon. If you'd bake some fudge brownies, Twila, I think that will be good enough."

The next morning they left early as planned, dropping Tanisha off at Uncle Jerry's first thing. Tanisha didn't seem to notice or care that she was being excluded from the family outing. In fact, Dad had told Tanisha that she was special to be singled out to spend the day at Uncle Jerry's house. Twila knew Tanisha was likely to cooperate much better in unfamiliar surroundings than she did at home, even though Uncle Jerry and Aunt Julia would not be deceived by her fake charm.

"It's going to be so much fun today!" exclaimed Suzanne as they headed north to Copper Falls. "So peaceful and quiet!"

"I'm sure it will be fun," Marilyn said wryly. "But I don't know about the quiet. We haven't had much of it yet."

"You know what I mean," Suzanne retorted. They all knew what she meant, and no one said anything more. Somehow, though they all agreed with Suzanne, it didn't seem right to be this happy about a day without Tanisha.

Rita was sitting next to Robbie in his car seat. "Sing, Rita," he pleaded. "Sing 'Jesus Loves Me.'" Rita started the song, and soon most of the others had joined in too. They went down through Robbie's favorites, which were not confined to children's songs. He also loved the songs "Joy to the World" and "Fill Up My Cup."

"Mama, I want a drink, please," Robbie requested.

While Mother dug through a basket of picnic supplies to find his sippy cup, Suzanne leaned around Rita and asked, "Why do you say *Mama?* Why don't you say *Mother* like all the rest of us do?"

Robbie shook his head. "Can't say Muzzer."

"Oh, yes, you can!" returned Suzanne. "I'll help you. Say it like this." Slowly and clearly she said, "Mo-ther," exaggerating the pronunciation.

Robbie tried, but it just didn't come out right. He took a long drink from the cup Mother handed to him and then settled sleepily into his car seat. "Can't say Muzzer. I'll just say Mama."

After some time Robbie fell asleep, but when they arrived at their destination, he woke up promptly. "I want out too!" he cried, afraid that he'd be left behind. Rita quickly helped him unbuckle, and they all piled eagerly out of the van. Before they rushed off, Dad gave them instructions on being careful and showed them on the map of trails where to go.

To get to the trails, they first had to cross an expanse of trees and lawn. At the foot of the wooded hill was Wild River. A wooden bridge crossed over it, and then they could walk the trails of Copper Falls State Park.

Happy to be let loose after riding for two hours, the younger girls and Robbie ran ahead. Marilyn and Twila weren't far behind.

Dad and Mother strolled leisurely after them. The trail forked, and the Hammond family took the right path that led to the falls. The first one was Copper Falls, which the park had been named after. The Wild River spilled over rocks, and the water flowing down had a coppery tint to it. A little farther down the trail was the Golden Falls. This waterfall had more of a brown coloring, and Twila didn't think it was quite as pretty as Copper Falls.

The little girls and Robbie leaned over the fence that ran as a protection along the trail and tried to see as much as possible of the breathtaking beauty below. Robbie stretched a little more and exclaimed, "Where does all that water go? I wish I could see down!" Marilyn's eyes twinkled at Twila when Mother clutched at Robbie's shirt and cautioned him to be careful. Mother always seemed to worry over things that were perfectly safe.

After taking some pictures of the falls, they backtracked to the fork in the trail and took the left path that led to the observation tower. Some places the path was flat, and in other places wooden stairways took them up the steep inclines. "Want me to carry you, son?" Dad offered. But Robbie shook his head. He clutched the handrail and continued up the steps, determined that his own two feet would carry him.

When Marilyn and Twila reached the tower, the younger girls were already partway up. They could hear them laughing and talking. By the time the older girls got to the top, they were thoroughly winded. Twila walked to the railing and looked out over miles of trees and hills. Winding through it was a thin trail of blue where the Wild River flowed.

"Isn't it just beautiful!" Marilyn exclaimed. "Come look through this spotting scope, Twila. You can see all the way to Lake Superior!"

Twila took a turn at the spotting scope, which was mounted on a pedestal. She turned it in different directions, trying to see all she could of the landscape. Then Connie wanted a chance to look, so she turned it over to her.

Hearing Robbie's voice down below, Twila commented, "Oh, Mother and Dad must be coming up."

Marilyn grinned. "I'm kind of surprised Mother's coming up. You know how she hates heights."

Twila walked over to the other side of the tower. As she went, she noticed Suzanne moving in slow cautious steps in the center of the tower where the railing cased the stairway coming up. She clutched the board railing, staying as far away from the outside edge as possible.

"What's wrong with you?" Twila asked in surprise. Suzanne just shook her head and refused to answer. It suddenly dawned on Twila that Suzanne was terrified. It was so uncharacteristic of Suzanne that she stared at her in amazement.

As soon as Dad and Mother made it all the way up, Connie informed them, "Suzanne is scared!"

"I'm not scared," Suzanne said defensively. "I just don't like it up here!"

Mother, who had taken a brief tour around the tower, told her, "It's okay to admit you're scared. I don't like heights myself. This makes me feel dizzy. I'm going down. Do you want to come with me?"

The two of them went down together, while the rest of them lingered, enjoying the scenery. After seeing everything there was to see, Dad, the other girls, and Robbie went back down.

From the tower, they followed the trail that meandered on through the leafy woods. Every so often there were benches where one could rest and signs that gave information about points of interest. After a while they came to the river again. The whole family stood together on the bridge and watched a fisherman pull in a shiny brown trout. He obligingly held it up so they could see it. He and Dad talked for a few minutes before the family moved on.

On this side of the river, it was dark, damp, and mosquitoey. Finally they reached the higher ground and the spot where the sign proclaimed it to be the highest point in the park. Down below they could see where the river wound around in a U shape, which was aptly named The Horseshoe.

They had been tramping for several hours now, and they were all getting tired and hungry. Robbie, who had determinedly trucked the whole way on his own short legs, sat down on a stump and refused to go one step farther.

Dad chuckled. "You did pretty good, walking all that way!" He picked up the little fellow and settled him on his shoulders. Robbie rode there the rest of the way back.

Twila was last in line as they walked along the final part of the trail. She contemplated how the beauty of God's creation, the sound of running water, and the pleasant family time seemed to be having a relaxing effect on them all. She reflected how much closer God seemed with the lack of conflict. Twila sighed. She hadn't felt this happy in a long time.

Arriving back at the van, they chose a picnic table nearby. Dad got a charcoal fire going to grill the hot dogs and hamburgers. Mother spread a cloth on the table, and the girls helped her set out the rest of the lunch so they could eat. After all that walking, they were hungry and ate heartily.

When they were finished, the younger girls and Robbie ran back to the bridge and waded in the shallow river water. Dad stretched out in the grass, tipped his cap over his face, and caught some sleep. The older girls helped Mother pack up the leftovers from lunch. When they were done, they crossed the bridge and wandered back up the short distance to the falls and took some more pictures.

An hour or so later, Dad decided it was time to go home. They all crawled back into the van somewhat reluctantly. It had been an enjoyable day, and they were sorry to see it end. Before Dad turned the key in the ignition, he glanced back at Suzanne. "Well, was the day as much fun as you thought it would be?"

Suzanne sighed. "It would have been if I wouldn't have felt so guilty for being glad that Tanisha wasn't along."

"You don't need to feel bad for being glad that Tanisha wasn't along," Dad said kindly. "Having a child like Tanisha in our home is a lot of hard work for all of us. In fact, Mrs. Gunther encouraged us to take a break once in a while. That way we'll have more energy to help Tanisha heal when she's with us. Of course, we don't want to be selfish about it. For Tanisha to learn to accept us as her family, she'll have to spend most of her time with us, especially Mother."

Twila leaned back in her seat. It was a relief to know she didn't have to feel ashamed for enjoying the day so much.

Marilyn spoke up. "Well, now that we've had a day's break, I think I feel ready to have Tanisha back with us again! Our family just doesn't feel complete without her."

Monday morning, the sun shone brightly through Twila's bedroom window. Twila bounced out of bed early, but noticed that even so, Marilyn was already up. She could hear the murmur of Mother's and Marilyn's voices coming from the kitchen. After dressing and combing her hair, she breezed into the kitchen where breakfast preparations were already underway.

An hour later, Mother took Tanisha and left for town. Today Tanisha had an appointment with a therapist to be evaluated. After her evaluation was completed, weekly therapy sessions would take place in the Hammond home. The Hammonds had offered up many prayers on Tanisha's behalf. Though her behavior continually grew worse, it seemed that God was answering their prayers one tiny step at a time. Now that Tanisha was starting therapy, the family felt encouraged and hopeful.

As Mother drove out the lane, Twila prayed that the therapist could be used of God to help Tanisha. She went to her room to hang some dresses in the closet. On the way, she paused at the door of the younger girls' room. Hanging on the wall was a motto Rita had made. She had decorated the edges of a piece of typing paper with colored flowers and leaves. In the center she had penciled in her childish hand, *God made everything buityful. Ecclesiastes 3:11.*

Twila stood still for a moment, pondering the words. Lately, it seemed like all her thoughts came back around to Tanisha. Could this verse possibly be talking about Tanisha who, with her broken little heart, never seemed to notice the beauty around her? On the outside, Tanisha was a beautiful child, but her actions certainly weren't beautiful. What was beautiful about children hurt by an uncaring world?

But the verse wasn't talking about what mankind had done to mess up God's creation. God *had* made everything beautiful, even Tanisha. It wasn't the little girl's fault that life had treated her so cruelly and damaged her responses to love and security. Was there a connection between this verse and the situation the Hammond family was facing with Tanisha? Twila wandered to her room, deep in thought. In the days to follow, she would find herself standing in the younger girls' bedroom many times, reading that verse.

Twila hung her dresses in the closet and then went outside to pick some flowers for the dining room table. Robbie trailed after her. He picked a fistful of dandelions and said, "I'm picking these Daniel-lions for Mama."

Twila and Robbie paused to smell the June roses. Their delicate fragrance drifted all over the backyard. Robbie gave a delighted sniff and said, "These flowers stink good!"

Twila laughed. "You mean they *smell* good!"

"They smell good!" Robbie corrected himself. He bent to sniff another flower and then straightened up with a sudden wail of pain. A bee had buzzed out of the roses and stung him right near the corner of his eye. Sobbing, he clutched at his face with both hands, his dandelions scattered at his feet.

Twila gently pulled his hands down and saw that his eyelid was already starting to swell. Picking Robbie up, she carried him in to Marilyn. The girls debated over what they should do for him. "Doesn't Mother sometimes use baking soda for bee stings?" Twila wondered.

"Yes, but the bee sting is so close to his eye, we'd end up getting soda in it and then Robbie would *really* howl," Marilyn objected. "Go get me a cold, wet washcloth. I'll put that on his eye for now. And there should be some salve in the bathroom cupboard that we can use for bee stings. Get me some of that too."

Twila went to get the wet washcloth and salve. Once the salve was applied, some of the pain seemed to go out of the sting, and Robbie calmed down.

Several evenings later, the Hammonds went to visit George and Ethel Hendricks, an elderly couple who often came to trade produce with them. George would bring over a bucket of crab apples and trade them for tomatoes. The crab apples were sweet and delicious, and the Hammond sisters loved to eat them.

When they arrived at the Hendricks', George came to meet them at the door. He shook their hands and cordially welcomed them in. Ethel sat at the kitchen table. When they walked in, she looked up at them with milky eyes. The years and cataracts had taken her sight, and now she could see only the outlines of things.

Mother leaned down and shook Mrs. Hendricks' hand, and then Mrs. Hendricks took Robbie's hand. "I got stung by a bee!" Robbie informed her.

"You did!" Ethel exclaimed. "What were you doing? Pounding on the beehives with a stick? When our children were small, we had bees," Ethel remembered. "I was out picking berries one day when our son Frank took a stick and started hitting the hives. I warned him to stop or he'd get bit. But he wouldn't listen. He said, 'Dem bees got no teef!' Well, he soon found out that bees have something every bit as bad at teeth," finished Ethel. They all chuckled over the story.

Connie shook Ethel's hand next, and when she mentioned that she was ten years old, Ethel asked her, "Can you say the alphabet backward? When I was ten, I had the measles and had to spend three weeks in bed. I got very bored, so for something to do, I learned to say the alphabet backward." To prove it, Ethel recited the alphabet backward for them.

Suzanne's eyes lit up. "I'm going to learn to do that!"

The Hendricks were an interesting couple to visit with. Though they were well into their nineties, their minds were still sharp. They remembered a lot of interesting happenings from years ago. After visiting for a while, Dad asked, "Would you like us to sing for you and read some Scripture?"

"Sure," answered George for both of them. "We don't get to church much anymore, and we'd be glad if you would." As they began singing, Twila noticed Mr. Hendricks' fingers tapping on the arm of his rocker in time to the music.

After several songs, Dad opened his Bible and read the familiar words of John 14, "Let not your heart be troubled: ye believe in God, believe also in me. In my Father's house are many mansions: if it were not so, I would have told you. I go to prepare a place for you." Dad finished reading John 14 and led in prayer. They sang a few more songs and visited awhile longer before going home. It had been an enjoyable evening.

CHAPTER TEN

God's Hands and Feet

Twila hung up her dish towel and turned to Marilyn. "I'm going out to shut the chicken house door."

"Better hurry," Marilyn replied. "I think Dad has something he wants to talk to us about."

A few minutes later, her job accomplished, Twila stepped into the peaceful quietness of the living room. Dad was in the big recliner, reading a newspaper. Mother was reading to Robbie and Tanisha. Robbie sat in Mother's lap, his head leaning contentedly against her shoulder. Tanisha sat beside Mother, her face empty of emotion. Marilyn had her nose in a book, and the three middle girls were poring over a doll magazine.

As Twila sank into a chair, Dad laid down his paper. "Got those chickens penned up?" he wondered.

Twila nodded. "I had to chase in that one black hen. I don't know why she won't go in of her own accord like all the other chickens."

"Some chickens just don't seem to want to be a part of the flock," Dad commented. For a moment his eyes rested gently on the stiff little figure beside Mother. Mother finished reading her story and went to tuck Tanisha into bed. Dad stood and retrieved a sheaf of papers from the end table. He sat down in the recliner and waited for Mother to return before announcing that he had something to say.

Marilyn's book dropped to her lap, and she looked up with an expression of mild curiosity. The younger girls shut their magazine and turned to face Dad.

"As you know," Dad began, "we've been making some changes around here since we've started therapy for Tanisha. The attachment therapist has been teaching Mother and me ways to help Tanisha heal emotionally. These methods will help her bond to us and form healthy attachments. You are all aware that I put an alarm on the door of Tanisha's room today. This alarm will ring and sound all over the house at night whenever anyone goes in or out of her room. Children who experienced neglect and trauma as babies have a lot of fears. An alarm helps them to feel safe because they know it will ring if anyone enters their room. An alarm will also keep us safe. Tanisha won't be able to get up at night and play with matches or other dangerous items without us knowing."

Dad looked around the room at the relieved expressions of the girls. "Mother and I also decided that it's very important for us to schedule our lives more closely than we've done before. We've written up a schedule for each of you girls for every day of the week." Dad rose from his chair and handed a paper to each of the girls, from Marilyn down to Rita.

Robbie glanced around the room with a look of disappointment. "Where's my paper?" he wondered.

Dad looked down at his small son. "Oh, that's right! You like to be included in everything, don't you? We need to remember that!"

"Here, Robbie," Marilyn said quickly. "You can share my paper with me." Robbie settled into her lap and pretended to read the paper that Marilyn held out in front of them.

Twila skimmed down over her schedule and noticed that every day was detailed out, from laundry and dish duty to lawn mowing, chicken chores, and cleaning.

Suzanne looked over her paper and groaned. "Do we actually have to get up at 6:30? That's way too early! I'll be so sleepy."

"Not a problem," said Dad calmly. "If you'll notice on your schedule, every afternoon you have two hours to read or do whatever you like. If you're too tired, you may take a nap instead."

"No . . . no," stammered Suzanne quickly. "That's okay. I don't think I'll be too tired."

Twila looked unhappily at her own paper. The schedule wasn't really so much different from what they already did, but it irked her that so much of what they did had to revolve around Tanisha.

Rita and Connie had some questions about their schedules. They didn't sound very excited either. Twila knew the only reason they weren't complaining was that they didn't want to risk being told they had to take naps.

Marilyn said cheerfully, "It won't be that bad. Just think of how much work we'll be able to get done if we're more organized. In the end, we should be able to have more free time than we did before. If it helps Tanisha feel more secure and settled, we'll be glad we did it."

"You're right," agreed Dad. "We want to do what we can so Tanisha can get better. Most of all, we want to trust God for healing. I want to read you a verse from the Bible."

Dad reached for his Bible and read the words of Jesus from Luke 4:18. "The Spirit of the Lord is upon me, because he hath anointed me to preach the gospel to the poor; he hath sent me to heal the brokenhearted, to preach deliverance to the captives, and recovering of sight to the blind, to set at liberty them that are bruised."

A healing hope washed over Twila as Dad read those words. Tanisha's healing depended on more than what Dad and Mother or they as a family tried to do for her. What they did was important, but ultimately it was God who healed. God cared about little

Tanisha, whose heart had been shattered by neglect and unkindness. He loved her more than they ever could.

Dad prayed for a long time, bringing each member of the family before the Lord, especially Tanisha. He prayed fervently that her captive heart would be freed from fear and anger, and that her brokenness could be mended. He asked that God would open her eyes to His love and the love of her family. He prayed earnestly for wisdom to raise all his children to love and serve God.

The next days and weeks were difficult as Dad and Mother lovingly placed more structure around Tanisha. She was no longer allowed to roam freely wherever she pleased. Instead of sending Tanisha to Sunday school with the other five-year-olds, Mother kept her by her side for the whole church service. Tanisha seldom played with the other children unless under strict supervision. Her meals, naps, and bedtimes were at the same time each day. At first, the little girl resisted the structure so fiercely that Twila wondered if it was really worth it.

One morning after a difficult session with Tanisha, Mother came out of the living room singing,

"What a day that will be when my Jesus I shall see,

When I look upon His face, the One who saved me by His grace..."[6]

"Why do you always sing that song after working with Tanisha?" wondered Twila.

Mother looked surprised. "What song?" Twila sang a line of the song Mother had just been singing.

Mother smiled. "I guess I do sing that song a lot, don't I? I suppose it's because it says so perfectly what I've been thinking and feeling lately. Several years ago when our baby Michael was still-born, Heaven seemed so near and dear that I wanted to go there more than I ever had before. Now, since Tanisha has come into our care, I've been thinking about Heaven even more. Every time Tanisha is extra difficult, I long for that day when we can all go to Heaven where hurting hearts will be healed . . . where innocent children no longer have to suffer."

"You know," Twila said, "that's something I've wondered about since Tanisha came. Why does God allow innocent children to be hurt? Why wouldn't a loving God protect them?"

"I've often pondered that myself," Mother replied. "We know that broken homes and abused children are not in God's plan. We also know that God has given everyone freedom of choice, and we don't always make good choices. It doesn't seem fair that so often little children are the victims of those choices. But we have to trust that God is good and He is just. We must believe Romans 8:28: 'And we know that all things work together for good to them that love God, to them who are the called according to his purpose.' We have to believe that in the end, He will make all things come out right. Meanwhile, we Christians have the privilege of being God's hands and feet to love and comfort these precious children."

Twila slowly turned the page of the flower catalog that had just come in the mail. She sighed. "I know I should consider it a privilege, but some days it feels like just plain old hard work."

"It *is* work," Mother agreed. "But if we can keep in focus what all God has done for us, loving one of His neglected children is the least we can do. There are many, many other Christians in the world making sacrifices and giving up the comforts of life for the sake of Christ. Why shouldn't we?"

"It's just that taking care of a child like Tanisha seems like such a thankless job," Twila replied. "She sure doesn't seem to appreciate what we do for her. And other people have no idea what it's like to live with her day after day. Most of them don't care, or if they do, they soon forget about it. And other people seem to think we exaggerate the whole thing, and that Tanisha is the poor little victim."

"I really think Tanisha is more grateful than she appears to be," Mother said. "She just doesn't know how to accept our love. She wouldn't be fighting it so much if she wasn't finding security in being in a loving home. And how much gratitude would be enough, anyway?" Mother wondered. "How grateful were the Indians when they killed Dr. Whitman and his wife after all their years of love and sacrifice among them?"[7]

Mother sorted through the stack of mail on the table. "I'm sure there are plenty of other stories of people who spent their lives helping others but received very little appreciation for what they did. When I'm exhausted and feel like I'm stretched to the limit, I like to remember that story in the Gospels where the unprofitable servant said, 'I have only done that which is my duty to do.' "

Twila flipped another page in the catalog and said thoughtfully, "So I guess we could say it this way: God doesn't owe us anything. We don't deserve to have things nice or easy. Whatever work God brings into our lives, we need to do. It's our gift of love back to Him for what He's done for us. And in the end, if Tanisha does get better, there's no praise or glory to us. God gets that. We were only doing what was our duty to do."

For a moment Mother's hand rested on Twila's shoulder. "You're right! Exactly right! When duty is done in love, it's no longer a duty, but something we willingly do."

---

7 In 1836 Marcus and Narcissa Whitman were among the first American settlers to go to Oregon as missionaries to the Indians. There they started churches and schools, and Mr. Whitman was also a doctor. In 1847 a measles epidemic broke out. Because the white people had immunity to the disease, not as many of them died as the Indians. Dr. Whitman was blamed, and he and his wife were killed by the Indians.

The peonies were blooming beautifully, and a few days later, Marilyn and Twila came into the house just as Mother was finishing braiding Tanisha's hair in cornrows. "Mother," Twila said, "may we take Tanisha out and take pictures of her and Robbie in front of the peony bed? We'd like to do it now while Tanisha's hair looks so nice."

Mother gave permission, and they happily trooped out to the flower bed. Twila straightened the collar on Robbie's shirt, and Marilyn had the two little children sit down just so. But no matter how much they coaxed and pleaded, Tanisha refused to smile. She just sat there stiffly with a blank expression on her face.

Finally Suzanne impulsively said, "Smile, Tanisha, so Grandpa Marilyn can take a picture of your messy hair!"

Before Tanisha could catch herself, she smiled, and Marilyn quickly snapped a picture. "There, I got one!" she said with satisfaction.

Twila took Tanisha back into the house, and Marilyn took some pictures of the three middle sisters. When she came back out, Twila picked an armful of peonies to take into the house. She began to artistically alternate the pink, white, and plum-colored flowers in a large vase.

Patrick walked past with his tail arched proudly and a gray field mouse clamped firmly in his jaws. His hair had started to grow back, but he still looked ridiculous. The wound on his leg had healed, but it had left a puckered purple scar. The hair would never grow over the scar, and it would always be conspicuous.

Suzanne watched the cat go by and complained, "I don't like cats, but it still makes me mad at Tanisha every time I see Patrick! I don't believe Tanisha really has anything wrong with her. I think all she needs is a good sound spanking, and that would take care of her problems. Mother and Dad sure never let us other children act like Tanisha does."

Twila looked critically at her flower arrangement and carefully nestled a white peony between a pink one and a plum-colored one. She turned to Suzanne. "Social Services has restrictions on the kind of discipline foster parents use. Spanking isn't allowed. You know that, Suzanne!"

Marilyn reached out and pinched Robbie's nose, making him laugh. She straightened up and looked at her sisters. "I asked Mother about that. From what she told me, Mother and Dad likely wouldn't spank Tanisha even if it was allowed, because spanking doesn't work very well for children with problems like Tanisha's. Until they heal enough to trust their parents, spanking may only make things worse. Mother says it's a little like trying to make someone walk on a broken leg."

"I heard Mother say there's no quick fix for children with problems like Tanisha's. She said it takes a lot of hard work," Rita said seriously.

"Well, why don't Dad and Mother use other kinds of punishments more?" Suzanne huffed. "And God can do anything, can't He? I wonder why He doesn't just heal Tanisha."

"I don't know," Marilyn said. "Maybe if God always performed miracles, people would get the idea they could live selfish, sinful lives, and afterward God would be there to take away the consequences of what they've done."

"The Bible says you reap what you sow," Twila added thoughtfully, remembering a conversation with Mother just a few days before. "Apparently, children sometimes have to bear the pain and consequences of what their parents have sown."

Marilyn tucked the camera back into its case. "I wonder? Maybe God will perform a miracle yet. We get impatient and want

God to do things right now. I think we just need to believe God will heal Tanisha in His own time, not ours."

Mother came to the back door and called for the girls. "Dad just phoned me and asked if I'd go to town and get some paint for him at the building supply store. I may be gone for a while. Marilyn, I have a batch of bread rising, so when it's ready, I'd like you to divide it into loaves and put it into pans."

"Are you taking Tanisha?" asked Suzanne. "I sure don't want to be stuck at home with her."

"Yes, I'm taking Tanisha with me," replied Mom. "And Suzanne, I know it's hard to always feel kindly toward Tanisha, but try to at least speak nicely of her."

Suzanne sighed but nodded obediently.

Mother gave final instructions and then took Tanisha and left. The girls and Robbie went inside. Indoors, things looked rather depressing. They had been very busy lately with the garden and outside work, and most of Mother's time was taken up with Tanisha. They hadn't been able to keep up with the housework as usual.

For a few moments, the girls rather aimlessly tried to decide how to entertain themselves while Mother was gone. Robbie was fussing because he wanted to go with Mother, and she had made him stay home.

Suddenly Rita's eyes lit up. "Robbie," she exclaimed, "let's make a house out of chairs and blankets!"

Robbie cheered, and soon the two of them were dragging chairs into the living room. They got blankets from a closet and draped them over the circle of chairs. They had a wonderful time as they dug out all the dolls and a bunch of toys from the toy box.

Suzanne looked disgustedly at the huge mess. "Don't expect me to help you clean that up!" She found a book, sat down amid the clutter, and started reading.

Marilyn looked into the bowl of bread dough and then glanced around the kitchen. "I suppose I really ought to wash these dishes," she remarked listlessly. She wandered over to the cookbooks and pulled one off the shelf. "I think I'm going to see if I can find something good to make for supper." She began leafing through its pages.

Connie got out her paper dolls and sat cross-legged in the middle of the dining room floor. She carefully laid out her dolls and their clothes in a circle around her.

Twila wandered to her and Marilyn's bedroom and then back out again as she tried to decide what she wanted to do. She went over to the stereo and pushed the button. "I know what I'm going to do," she exclaimed suddenly. "I'm going to make a pillow for my bed."

She went to the sewing room, pulled out a box of fabric scraps, and took it out to the table. Before long, she had fabric scattered all over as she rummaged through it, trying to decide what colors she wanted for her pillow. Eventually she settled on shades of green and burgundy. She got a three-inch square pattern and began marking blocks for the pillow top.

Twila had just starting cutting out the blocks she had traced, when she happened to look out the window and saw a car driving in the lane. She jumped up and went to the window to see who it was. She gasped, "Great-Uncle Noah and Aunt Alta are here!" These elderly relatives visited about twice a year, seldom calling ahead to say they were coming. Aunt Alta's crippled leg would prevent them from arriving at the door quickly.

Marilyn leaped up from the table where she was still looking at cookbooks and glanced frantically around the house, which was cluttered from one end to the other. She had put the bread into pans, but had not done any dishes. "Girls, quick!" she cried. "We've got to clean up this house!"

The girls sprang into action. Twila scooped up her sewing things and stuffed them back into the box. She carried it back to the sewing room and then hurried to help clean up the rest of the house.

Connie snatched up her paper dolls. Suzanne made the toys fly in the general direction of the toy box, fuming, "I don't know why Robbie and Rita had to make such a horrible mess anyway! Now *I* have to help them clean it up." She grabbed a stack of books and shoved them into the bookcase. "Why did they have to dig out a whole shelf of books?"

She straightened and kicked several stuffed animals toward the toy corner, continuing her tirade, "And people ought to know that you don't drop in unexpectedly to visit when a family has a child like Tanisha living with them. Why couldn't they call first?" She grabbed two chairs and shoved them up to the table, panting from the exertion of flying around the living room. "And they definitely shouldn't come when Mother's gone," she added.

Connie grabbed an armload of blankets and hauled them off to a bedroom to be stashed out of sight. "They probably don't even know about Tanisha's problems," she said reasonably.

In the kitchen, Marilyn clattered the dishes into a big dishpan and hid them under the sink. She quickly wiped off the counter tops, and in a couple of minutes, the kitchen looked much better.

By the time Uncle Noah and Aunt Alta reached the porch, most of the clutter was gone, and the appearance of the house was drastically improved. From the oven came the inviting aroma of bread baking.

Trying hard to appear calm and collected instead of flushed and out of breath, Marilyn went to the door and welcomed their visitors. She explained that Mother wasn't home and then helped Aunt Alta climb the steps into the house. She led them to the living room so they could sit down.

Twila was very glad Marilyn was there to help visit. She tried to help Marilyn out, but kept glancing nervously toward the window to see if Mother was driving in the lane. Twila and her sisters dearly loved this kindly aunt and uncle, and they had never minded before when they dropped in unexpectedly. But since Tanisha had come to live with them, unannounced visitors only added to the tension of dealing with a troubled child.

The girls relaxed a little when they learned that their visitors were planning to go to Uncle Loren's for lunch and to Grandma Hammond's house for supper that evening. At least they weren't expected to come up with a meal without Mother's help!

Fifteen minutes later, Mother drove in the lane, and Twila felt much relieved. But the relief was short-lived. Tanisha took one look at their elderly visitors, whom she'd never seen, and promptly went to sit beside Uncle Noah. "I'm so glad you came to visit," she gushed. "You're the nicest uncle in the whole world. I'm so glad you're my uncle!" As she chattered, Twila observed that Uncle Noah was quite captivated by the little girl.

"Tanisha," Mother said, quietly but firmly. "Come sit here beside me." Uncle Noah and Aunt Alta exchanged puzzled looks at Mother's insistent tone, and for a moment an awkward silence filled the room.

Uncle Noah and Aunt Alta stayed for about an hour, and then it was time for them to go to Uncle Loren's.

Mother walked with them to the door. She helped Aunt Alta down the steps and out to the car. Marilyn slipped a loaf of fresh bread into the back seat. Since Aunt Alta was getting more and more crippled, she could no longer make her own bread.

Everyone waved goodbye, and as the car pulled out of the lane, Twila felt the strain of the last hour slowly drain away. It was short-lived, however. Going to town and then coming home to company had been too much for Tanisha. When Mother told her to go play with her dollhouse while she went to the kitchen to get lunch ready, Tanisha stood perfectly still for a moment. Then she fell apart.

As soon as Mother left the room, she flew to the dollhouse, snatched up her favorite doll, and flung it across the room. More dolls and dollhouse furniture were hurled after it in rapid succession. When there was nothing left to throw, Tanisha gave the dollhouse a shove, knocking it over on its side. Then she flopped on the floor herself, kicking and pounding the floor and emitting loud sobs.

Hearing Tanisha's crying and Rita's and Connie's shouts of alarm, Mother hurried back into the living room. She calmly picked up the sobbing child and took her to the rocking chair. She rubbed Tanisha's back and murmured soothingly, "It's okay. I'll hold you till you're done crying. It's okay."

Twila was amazed and relieved when Tanisha allowed Mother to comfort her. Gradually her wild crying stopped. She sat rocking herself back and forth on a kitchen chair while Mother heated up some leftovers for lunch.

Later that afternoon, when the girls' free time was over, Mother told Twila, "I'd like you to make some whoopie pies. When they're cool, wrap them individually and stack them in the blue container and put them in the freezer. They'll last longer that way."

Twila found a cookbook and began pulling out baking ingredients. As she measured and mixed, her mind wandered back to the question Suzanne had asked earlier that day. Why *didn't* Mother and Dad more often use consequences other than spanking for Tanisha's defiant behavior? They had never relied on any certain kind of discipline for the rest of their children.

She was beginning to frost the cookies when Mother came into the kitchen to get the broom. Twila paused in her work.

"Mother, you know how naughty Tanisha is. I know you can't spank her, but why don't you use other kinds of punishments for her like you did for the rest of us?"

Mother stopped in the doorway. "Do you think more punishments would change Tanisha's behavior?" she asked.

Twila slowly spread frosting on another cookie as she pondered that question. She thought of the time she had complained about the food at supper, and Dad had told her she couldn't have any dessert. She remembered another time when she had done such a sloppy job of weeding in the garden that Mother had made her weed an extra row. She had learned that whining and sloppiness weren't worth it, and she had tried to improve. But she still had a long way to go.

Twila put the top cookie on the whoopie pie and laid it on the table. "No, I doubt that more punishment would help much. But isn't there something you can do to make Tanisha behave?"

Mother absently ran the broom over a square of linoleum before answering. "When I think about disciplining a child like Tanisha, I think about how God dealt with the children of Israel whom He had chosen as His special people. After He had delivered them from slavery in Egypt and began leading them through the wilderness, He did give them consequences—sometimes very harsh consequences—for their obstinacy. But He never abandoned them. He was constantly with His people in the pillar of cloud or fire.

"Through the whole Bible, we see God longing for a relationship with His people. And that is what Dad and I are trying to build with Tanisha—a loving, trusting relationship. Until Tanisha has learned to trust us to love her no matter what, all the discipline in the world isn't going to change her. We can't punish away all the deviant behavior that is rooted in Tanisha's early experiences."

Twila looked at Mother in surprise. "So that means we just have to let her do whatever she wants?"

"No," said Mother. "It means we need to set her up for success. We limit her contact with other children so she can't hurt or manipulate them. We're not letting her go to Sunday school right now, and we realize that looks harsh to some people. Dad and I keep Tanisha close to one of us all day long. We expect that our constant presence and close supervision will eventually bring a sense of security to Tanisha."

Mother paused. "In a way you could say that this strict supervision is a consequence for Tanisha's behavior. But I'd rather think of it as an opportunity to build the relationship with Tanisha that she never had with her biological parents."

Twila nodded. Mother's explanation made sense. She wanted to ask more questions, but at that moment, Suzanne came bursting into the house with the mail. "Mother!" she shouted. "Do you know anyone by the name of Daniel Burkholder?"

Mother came into the kitchen and took the envelope from Suzanne. "No, I don't believe I do," she replied. She found a knife to slit open the envelope while Suzanne shifted impatiently from one foot to the other.

Inside the envelope was a sheet of typing paper. Mother silently read what it contained before handing it to Suzanne. Suzanne read aloud,

"You are invited!

To: An Adoption Fellowship Picnic

Date: August 10

Time: 10:00 a.m.

Place: Oakwood Park

We will provide the hot dogs, ice cream, and drinks. Bring along a snack or a cold dish to share. Please call and inform us of how many plan to come."

At the bottom of the page was a phone number and directions for how to get to the park.

"Oh, Mother!" exclaimed Suzanne. "That sounds like so much fun. Do you think we'll be able to go?"

"I don't see why not," Mother replied. "I don't know that we have anything planned for August tenth, but of course we'll have to see what Dad says."

Suzanne took the invitation and attached it to the refrigerator with a magnet. "Oh, I hope we can go! Don't you, Twila?"

Twila nodded. "It does sound interesting!"

When Tanisha woke from her afternoon nap, Mother brought her into the kitchen and sat her down at the table with a picture and a few crayons. "Twila, while you finish your baking, I'm going to leave Tanisha here to color a picture while I go out and cut some garden lettuce. It will take me only a few minutes."

Twila took the last pan of cookies from the oven and washed up her baking dishes, keeping a sharp eye on Tanisha. She could cause trouble in the shortest amount of time of any child Twila had ever seen. But the minutes ticked by, and Tanisha quietly kept coloring her picture. *The structure and schedule that Mother and Dad are using must be starting to work,* Twila mused as she frosted the last of the cookies. Tanisha had allowed Mother to comfort her earlier, and now she was coloring quietly.

Mother entered the kitchen with her bowl of lettuce, and Suzanne came in behind her with some radishes. As she passed the table, Suzanne paused to look over Tanisha's shoulder. Seeing the neatly colored page, Suzanne exclaimed, "Wow, Tanisha! Good job. That looks really nice!"

Quick as a wink, Tanisha snatched up a black crayon and scribbled over the page. Suzanne turned to Mother, bewilderment written all over her face.

Mother didn't say anything. She simply went to a drawer and pulled out another picture for Tanisha to color. "Let's try it again," she told Tanisha. Her voice was calm. "Let's see if you can do it without spoiling the picture when you're done. And," Mother added, "Suzanne, could you run out to the garden and get me a couple of onions? I forgot to get some when I was out there."

Tanisha slowly colored another picture. When she was done, Mother said matter-of-factly, "There now! You're all done, and you only went out of the lines two times. I'm going to hang this on the refrigerator."

Later when Tanisha was out of hearing, Mother said, "Suzanne, I think you're wondering why Tanisha scribbled her picture when you told her it looked nice."

"Why *did* she do that?" Twila wondered. "I've noticed before that when we compliment her for something, she immediately starts doing the opposite."

"Compliments mean love and relationships," explained Mother. "But Tanisha struggles to connect emotionally with anyone, so I think family relationships must seem very scary to her. Possibly sometime in Tanisha's life, someone used compliments to harm her or take advantage of her. So now when she gets a compliment, maybe she associates it with danger in her mind."

"I don't really understand, but I'll try to be more careful after this," remarked Suzanne.

"But aren't we to praise her at all?" wondered Twila. "Isn't it good for any child to be told when they do a good job?"

"Tanisha will need to learn to accept praise," agreed Mother. "But until she gets used to it, we'll need to use a milder approach. And it's important to only compliment her on things she's done, never on things that she has no say over—such as her looks or her clothes. And then the praise must be given simply, so she doesn't feel threatened."

That evening when Dad came home from work, he noticed the picture on the refrigerator. "Someone did a very nice job of coloring!" he commented.

"Yes," agreed Mother. "Tanisha did that. I thought she did very well."

Both Mother and Dad carefully avoided making eye contact with Tanisha, pretending she wasn't there to hear what they said. Twila noticed a pleased glimmer in the little girl's eyes. *So that's what Mother meant by a more gentle approach to praise,* thought Twila. *She seems happy about it, so that must be the right way to do it.*

The next day after lunch Mother glanced at the clock. "Tanisha's therapist is coming in about an hour. I'm planning to take a nap before she gets here. Until then, you girls may do as you like."

Twila quickly rummaged in a drawer to find her painting supplies. She wanted to go out and see if she could paint a picture of their house.

Suddenly from the younger girls' bedroom came shouts, thumping, and a yowl from Patrick. As Mother headed for her bedroom door, the cat streaked into the dining room, and Rita bent to pick him up. He leaped into her arms. Suzanne burst into the room, hot on Patrick's heels. The cat tensed, ready to spring.

Rita's eyes flashed with uncharacteristic spunk. "Don't you kick my cat!" she exclaimed.

Suzanne was just as upset. "I did *not* kick your cat! All I did was give him a smack and tell him to get off *my* bed. Now there's cat hair on my blanket. It's so disgusting to have a cat in the house! Mother, can't you tell Rita to keep her cat out of the house?"

"How could he possibly have put any hair on your bed?" flashed Rita. "He hardly even *has* any hair! Tanisha cut it off."

"Well, there *was* cat hair on my bed!"

Suzanne would have said more, but Mother gave her a look. "You girls quit shouting at each other, right now!" she said firmly. "Suzanne, Dad said he doesn't care if Patrick is in the house so long as he's not scratching up the furniture. And Rita, if you want to have the cat in the house, see to it that he doesn't lie on Suzanne's bed. Go and shut the bedroom door so he can't get in there."

The argument was settled, and Mother went to take a nap. Suzanne cast one more dark look at Rita and the cat before going outside. Twila followed with her artwork supplies. Rita went to shut the bedroom door as she had been told.

An hour later, Twila looked up from her painting to see a car drive up the lane. She quickly picked up her stuff and went into the house to see if Mother was awake.

When the therapist entered the house, Twila immediately knew she would like her. Mrs. Gunther was kind and courteous, but she always carried herself with a businesslike, professional air. This lady was jolly and friendly. She shook hands with all the girls and introduced herself as Mrs. Patty Peters. "But," she said, "most people just call me Miss Patty. I've been an attachment therapist for ten years, and let me assure you, it's very rewarding work."

As they walked to the living room to sit down, Twila's doubt must have shown on her face, because Miss Patty looked at her and laughed gaily. "You're wondering why anyone would choose a profession of working with difficult children day after day."

Twila nodded sheepishly. Miss Patty sobered and said seriously, "It's because in my work, I've seen that these children can recover. I've seen broken and hurting children become whole and healthy again! These children can heal, but they have to want to. And that's my job—to help them *want* to overcome their harmful, destructive ways."

"I'm sorry Tanisha isn't up yet from her nap," Mother said as they entered the living room. "I'll go and get her."

"When does she normally wake up?" wondered Miss Patty.

Mother glanced at the clock. "Not for another fifteen minutes."

"Then don't waken her. If you don't mind, I'd like to talk to the rest of you before I begin the session with Tanisha."

Mother nodded her assent, and Miss Patty turned to the girls. "I'm sure your parents have explained to you what reactive attachment disorder is, and you've seen firsthand the behavior that goes along with it. I'd like to explain some things you girls can do to help, because helping a child with this problem is all about everyone working together—the family, church, and community. Since we want Tanisha to bond with your mom, most of the interaction with her falls to Mom. Remember, you should never do anything for Tanisha or give anything to her without permission from Mom. Not even a tissue or a piece of candy. Tanisha needs to learn, just like a little baby, that all good things come from Mom. She needs to see Mom as her source of food, comfort, and love, just as a newborn baby very quickly learns."

Miss Patty smiled at the girls. "Now here's a *fun* thing you girls can do. I'm sure you know how good a child like Tanisha is at taking the joy and happiness out of your home. Don't let Tanisha do this! Find things to be happy about. Go out of your way to add laughter to the day. It's very important for Tanisha to be surrounded by happiness so she can get better."

Miss Patty was about to let them go, and then she remembered one more thing. "Oh, yes!" she exclaimed. "Above all else, keep alert for anything positive you see in Tanisha. It may help if you write it down or keep a list. This will help you not to dwell on the negatives so much."

As Miss Patty talked, more pieces fit into the confusing picture of what was wrong with Tanisha. She spoke with such encouragement and hope that Twila felt her spirits lift.

CHAPTER ELEVEN

The Forgivingest People in the World

Twila and her sisters hurried to get ready so they could go to Grandma Hammond's. This Saturday's event had been planned for some time. Grandma's family was getting together to put a new roof on her house.

Dad had left early to get prepared for the many hands that would be helping with the work. Because of his carpentry skills, the job of spearheading the whole project had naturally fallen to him.

Tanisha whined and complained. "I don't want to go along. I don't like those people, and it will be so boring! I just want to stay home." Twila knew Mother and Dad had debated whether or not to take Tanisha to the Hammond gathering. In the end, they had decided that Mother would bring her for the morning. After lunch, she and Tanisha would go home for a nap and a quiet afternoon, returning later in time for supper.

Marilyn finished up the last of the food that would be their contribution to the meals for the day. Mother combed the girls' hair, and at last they were ready to go.

Twila limped out to the van with the rest. She had sprained her foot the evening before, and today it was still painful. It would limit her activities for the day. and she was disappointed that it had to happen right before a Hammond gathering.

She felt herself tensing as they got closer to Grandma Hammond's. Tanisha was still insisting she didn't want to go to

Grandma's. What would she say and do once she got to Grandma's and was surrounded by sympathetic uncles, aunts, and cousins?

As they pulled into Grandma's lane, Tanisha's pouting face suddenly turned amiable. It was disgusting, the way Tanisha could be perfectly horrid at home and then turn into smiling sweetness the instant they got to their destination. At Hammond gatherings, she would hug Grandma, the aunts, and anyone else who happened to be near.

But this time, Tanisha was in for a surprise. Dad had talked to all of the extended Hammond family beforehand and asked them not to engage Tanisha in conversation, other than a simple hello when they first saw her. He had requested that there be no hugs either until Tanisha had healed enough to enjoy hugs from Mother.

As the girls and Mother entered the house, Grandma welcomed them warmly. There were greetings from other aunts and cousins who had arrived before them.

Tanisha danced forward to give Grandma a hug. "Oh, Grandma, I was so excited to come to your house today! I could hardly wait to get here."

Grandma hesitated a moment and then stepped back. "Hello, Tanisha. I'm very glad you could come too!" she said kindly. Then she turned to the other girls.

Tanisha stopped in her tracks. This rebuff was not what she had anticipated. Undaunted, she turned to pour her charm on other family members. Each time, there was a moment of awkwardness as the Hammond aunts, uncles, and cousins tried to respect Dad and Mother's wishes for Tanisha. Twila felt sorry for them. Tanisha did appear so sweet. She could see why it was hard for them to keep their greetings brief and cool.

Twila hobbled over to the couch and sat down. Grandma pushed a stool over for her to prop her foot on and clucked over her as Twila told how she had injured her ankle. "The other girls and I were playing hide-and-seek last evening. I was running in the dark, and I couldn't see that there was a slight dip in the ground," she explained. "I landed on the side of my foot and twisted my ankle. That was the end of hide-and-seek for me."

Tanisha was not happy to see the attention focused on Twila instead of her. Twila watched the little girl deliberately fall and start crying, as if she had accidentally tripped. Twila knew she couldn't have possibly hurt herself badly enough to merit the pathetic tears that dripped off her chin. Mother immediately pulled Tanisha to her feet and led her into another room, away from sympathetic glances.

Twila turned to Grandma. "I sure don't understand Tanisha. This morning before we came, she kept whining and complaining that she didn't want to come to your house. She said it would be boring."

Grandma looked troubled as she replied, "But when Tanisha got here, she told me how excited she was to come today. I can definitely see why your father requested that we limit our contact with her. But we'll keep praying for her. There's no doubt in my mind that somewhere there's a sweet child inside of her. God can heal her heart. I know He can."

"Do you really believe God will heal her, Grandma?" Twila asked doubtfully.

Grandma smiled and said firmly, "Yes, I really do! God's power is unlimited, and He loves Tanisha more than we do." As Grandma bustled back out to the kitchen to help with meal preparations, Twila tucked her words away in a corner of her mind to pull out sometime when she was discouraged.

The men and boys worked on the roof all morning, and the girls and any of the aunts who weren't working on the noon meal cleaned out Grandma's storage shed and weeded some flower beds. When that was done, they went across the lawn to Aunt Julia's and helped with her yard work.

Twila sat in the house and listened to the happy talk and laughter floating in through the open window. She longed to be outside in the middle of all the activity. Through the window, she could see Ricky and two other cousins pausing to get drinks from a water jug that had been set on a table for the busy workers. A water fight broke out, and there were shouts of laughter until fatherly voices drifted down from the roof, reminding the boys to stop playing and finish their job of cleaning up the old shingles.

Awhile later Grandma came into the living room and sat down. "The girls chased me out of the kitchen, so I thought I might as well come in and visit with you . . . and Markie too," she added, smiling a welcome as Aunt Bess came into the room with Markie.

As usual, Twila's Down syndrome cousin was full of sympathy for anyone who was hurt. "Poor Twila!" he said, patting her head.

A married cousin entered the room with her two-year-old and her baby boy. Twila eagerly took the baby. She played patty-cake and peekaboo with him, coaxing some baby chuckles out of him. He was so cuddly and cute! His bright eyes looked even bluer with the blue shirt he was wearing.

Grandma tucked his older sister in beside her on the big recliner and read story after story. Markie sat on the floor beside Grandma's chair and listened too. It wasn't long before more grandchildren and great-grandchildren were perched on the arms of the chair, absorbed in the stories.

Lunchtime came and everyone gathered around to pray and then eat. Marilyn brought a plate of food into the living room for Twila. The other cousins her age gathered nearby to eat, so Twila didn't feel like she was totally missing out on the fun.

After lunch, the men went back to their work on the roof and the women washed up the dishes and finished various projects they had started in the morning. Cousin Janet came into the house and told Twila, "We girls are working in the flower bed right beside Uncle Jerry's front porch. We'll give you a ride over in the garden cart, and you can sit on the porch swing while we work." Twila hopped out of the house and, giggling and laughing, the other girls pushed her over.

Markie tagged along, overseeing Twila's ride. "Be careful! Don't dump her out," he cautioned.

The roof was all done by suppertime. So after they had eaten, the young people and younger cousins went to play volleyball at a net the boys had set up in the yard. The women finished the dishes, and the men gathered up the last of the tools and did a few other fix-it projects for Grandma.

Unable to play volleyball with the rest of the cousins, Twila sat on the floor in the corner of the living room by the bookcase and pulled out a book to read. Soon Mother, the aunts, and Grandma came in and settled into chairs. They had apparently been talking about Tanisha, because Aunt Faith was saying, "Is it possible for a child to be that two-faced? She's so little. Only five years old! It sounds like something only an older child or even an adult would be capable of."

Mother sat quietly for a minute before answering. "Tanisha is a very strong, intelligent child. If she had been weak or unable to live by her wits, she probably wouldn't be here today. In her mind, the fact that she survived makes her feel that she's in control. Children like Tanisha have been betrayed by the adults in their lives, but they've lived through it. Such children distrust their adult authorities, especially a mother figure, because in their past, the mother and other adult caregivers neglected to meet their needs. Because Tanisha learned to get what she needed by conniving and manipulating, she has developed the habit of making her authorities, especially me, look bad."

Mother paused and then went on. "Think of a time in your life when someone betrayed you or let you down. We quickly learn not to trust that person. Think also of what it would be like to be a child who is denied the most basic needs of love, care, and food over and over again. Would you keep trying to get what you need from the people you live with? A child who is chronically neglected is apt to resist a loving connection with a new mother figure, sometimes to an unbelievable degree."

"Why does a child with this disorder resist the mom more strongly than the dad?" wondered Aunt Julia.

Mother smoothed the top of a couch cushion she was holding in her lap. She looked up at the circle of ladies around the room. "Because a baby is carried first in a mother's womb. Those who study child development believe that even in the womb, a child senses its mother's acceptance or rejection. God designed that after birth, the mother is to be the primary caregiver of her newborn child. The baby instinctively turns to its mother as the source of food, love, and comfort. This is the way God planned it. But when a mother deliberately or ignorantly refuses to fill her God-given role, the child grows up neglected and unloved, and this often produces tragic results. Children with attachment difficulties do resist connecting with their fathers, but often it is different from the way they relate to their mothers. They sometimes use Dad to manipulate and turn against Mom."

Aunt Carol spoke up. "It's hard to believe Tanisha's behavior is as bad as you describe it, because we just haven't see her behaving like that. I think you should be thankful you have such a sweet little girl. If I restricted my children from being with other people like you do Tanisha, they would resist me too. You won't let her go to Sunday school, and now Alex says we're not allowed to interact with her other than saying hello when we see her."

Twila felt sick, and Mother looked as if she'd been slapped.

Grandma spoke up slowly. "I remember how confused we all were when Ricky came with all his problems. I think the rest of us should reserve judgment until we know a little more about this."

Before Mother could answer, Aunt Bess said, "I don't want to support something that isn't right, but I do know how much it has meant to Will and me to have the support of family and church for the decisions we've made concerning Markie. Some of you haven't always understood why we chose to do things the way we did, but you supported us anyway. The least we can do now is stand by Alex and Mary Ann until we see evidence that it would be wrong to do so."

"Yes, I feel too that we should support them," agreed Aunt Julia. "I don't pretend to know or understand everything Alex and Mary Ann are going through. But Jerry and I know what it's like to have a challenging child. It meant so much to us through the years to have the compassion and understanding of church and family. If you ever need someone to talk to, Mary Ann, feel free to call me. I won't have a lot of advice, but I can give you a listening ear."

Aunt Carol, as though sensing the unspoken rebuke of the other ladies in the room, said hesitatingly, "I don't want to be hasty in my judgment. I still don't understand the advice your therapist is giving you, but in the meantime, Tim says we'll respect your wishes."

There were tears in Mother's eyes as she said, "Thank you! Thanks to all of you! And please . . . don't forget to pray for us. We so often feel at a loss to know how to best relate to Tanisha, and we desperately need God's help. I understand your doubts and fears about the restrictions we are imposing on Tanisha's social interactions. We've had to work through our own concerns about using these methods. But so far, the foster care agency hasn't recommended anything that goes against Biblical parenting methods. And we've seen enough small steps in the right direction that we're encouraged to keep on."

It was later than usual when they got to sleep that night, and the next morning, it was hard to pull themselves out of bed. But Dad saw to it that the family was up, ready, and at church on time.

Twila's foot was still bothering her, so rather than limp to the front of the church with the other girls her age, she sat in the back with Mother.

Church was over and they were almost ready to leave when Judy Weber came up to greet Mother. Twila liked Judy. She was always cheerful and friendly. "I hear you've put Tanisha in therapy because she's a very stubborn, difficult child," she was saying. "I wouldn't get too worried about it if I were you. Our oldest son was a very challenging child too. I wish I would have relaxed and not worried over him like I did. Today he's such a blessing to us. All he needed was lots of love and firm discipline and time to grow up. I'm sure that's all Tanisha needs as well."

Judy Weber breezed away, and Twila was left to wonder if she still liked her. When they got to the van, Dad scooped up Robbie and Tanisha and began buckling them into their car seats. Rita, who had also overheard Judy Weber's remarks, asked Mother, "Do the Webers have children with RAD too?"

"No," Mother said quietly. "Some people don't understand what attachment disorder really is. They want to compare a child with normal, healthy emotions to a child with unhealthy reactions to love and comfort. That's just not fair. We've had a lot to learn ourselves, and we need to be patient with others who are still learning."

After eating Mother's delicious Sunday dinner, Dad helped her put the two youngest children down for naps, and then he left in the van.

"Where's Dad going, Mother?" wondered Marilyn as she stacked the dinner plates together and carried them into the kitchen.

"He's going to a meeting with the ministers and some of the other men from church," replied Mother. "They have some questions about the methods we're using to deal with Tanisha's behavior."

"Why don't people believe what you and Dad say? Why can't they just trust you?" There was hurt and frustration in Marilyn's voice. "It makes me angry when people try to make it sound like it's all your fault, Mother. This morning I overheard someone say that you're the one with problems, not Tanisha."

Suzanne was helping clear the table, but she stopped at Marilyn's comment, eyes ablaze with indignation. "Well, I think that was a nasty thing to say!" she exploded. "They don't know what they're talking about!"

"Hush," said Mother firmly. "That's the point. They don't understand."

Some of the fire died in Suzanne's eyes, but she added, "Well, all I can say is that families who have difficult children have to be the forgivingest people in all the world. Forgive, forgive, forgive. And I don't feel one bit forgiving!"

"Well, sometimes I don't either," Mother said with a sigh.

Suzanne's mouth dropped open. "You don't?"

"No," Mother said, "I don't. But forgiving is a choice, not a feeling. I need to choose to forgive. I ask the Lord to help me, because I certainly can't do it myself."

Suzanne's expressive eyes shone with sudden understanding. "Well, I'm so glad you told me that, Mother," she said matter-of-factly. "Now I think there's a little hope for me."

"And maybe a little hope for the rest of us," Twila whispered to Marilyn, who was standing near her, the stack of plates still in her hands. Forgiving other people's thoughtless remarks was something they all struggled with.

Suzanne gave a happy little skip and left the room, saying she was going to find Connie.

Marilyn suddenly laughed. "Mother, did you ever think about it that Suzanne somehow always seems to say clearly what the rest of us have a hard time putting into words?"

Mother nodded. "Yes, she sure does. The 'forgivingest people in all the world,'" she repeated with a smile. "Now that is something to think about!"

And to live up to, Twila thought, as she picked up two serving bowls of leftover food and carried them out to the kitchen.

"I'm sorry you girls had to hear some of the negative comments from family and church people," Mother said a little later. "Dad and I had hoped to protect you from it as much as possible. But like Suzanne says, this is where forgiveness comes in. Different circumstances happen to different people. Some of the problems other people face, I have never faced. How many times have I been critical of someone, maybe even just in my heart, over something I know nothing about? We must not hold resentment against people when they don't understand."

"I suppose," said Marilyn, "that we should remember how clueless we were at first too. Remember how cute and sweet we thought Tanisha was? It took us awhile to find out all the problems that lay beneath that sweetness."

It was late when Dad came home. Robbie and Tanisha were already up from their naps and Mother was making popcorn for supper when Dad came in the door. There was a lightness to his step and a look of peace on his face that Twila hadn't seen for a while. She suddenly caught a glimpse of the burden that Dad carried for his family.

Dad sank into a chair with a sigh. He must have seen the questioning looks of his family, for he said, "The meeting went very well. They asked me to explain to them what we've been experiencing. They had a lot of questions afterward, but for the most part, the brethren were very supportive. I'm sure more things will come up in the future, but praise God! We were able to work through the issues that came up today."

Twila glanced at Tanisha and wondered if she understood anything Dad had said. She sat in her chair with her bowl of popcorn perched precariously on her knees. How cute and sweet she looked, with her hair frizzy from her nap and a sleepy look still in her eyes. Tanisha looked up to see Twila gazing at her and instantly made a face at her. Just as quickly, in a spirit of fun, Twila promptly made one back. Twila's heart was warmed to glimpse a teasing sparkle in the little girl's eyes before she turned and held up her bowl to Mother for more popcorn.

Rita finished her popcorn and took her bowl out to the kitchen sink. When she came back, she knelt in front of Tanisha. "Here, Tanisha. Let me do something."

Tanisha sat still while Rita took her fist and lightly tapped her forehead, saying, "Knock, knock." She gently pulled up one of Tanisha's eyelids and said, "Peek in!" Then taking her thumb, Rita tipped up the end of Tanisha's nose. "Open the door latch." Last of all, she poked a finger in Tanisha's mouth and added, "Walk in."

Tanisha smiled faintly, and Rita grinned back. "Want me to do it again?"

Tanisha leaned away from Rita. "No," she said firmly.

Rita looked puzzled. "Why not? It's fun to play games!"

Tanisha was quiet for a long moment, studying Rita's face. The rest of the family held their breaths, waiting for Tanisha to answer. It seemed as though she was searching inwardly for an answer she scarcely knew herself. Finally she said, "Because . . . because I don't like people touchin' me. I'm not used to it. I want everyone to stay away from me."

Rita stared thoughtfully at Tanisha. At last she spoke, "Well, if you would let me play it again, then you could get used to it."

But Tanisha shook her head decidedly. "Nope! I'm not lettin' you."

Robbie crowded in beside the two girls and pleaded, "Do it to me, Rita! Do it to me!" So Rita turned and played the game with Robbie instead.

In spite of Tanisha's aversion to Rita's touch, Twila noticed the interest in her eyes as she watched Rita and Robbie. *Tanisha is changing! She truly is changing!* Twila marveled.

The next morning Twila stood looking at the calendar. "It's hard to believe it's July already. This summer sure is going fast!" she said to Marilyn. "Before we know it, it'll be time to go back to school."

"I know," agreed Marilyn. "Mother wanted to cut out some school dresses this afternoon. She doesn't want to have a lot of sewing to do right over the busiest part of canning season. But then we remembered that I'm supposed to go to Mrs. Graham's today, and we have peas to pick. I don't think we'll have time for everything."

"Yes, and I don't think it's a bit fair," complained Suzanne, coming into the house. "Since Twila hurt her ankle and you're going to Mrs. Graham's, it will be just Mother and us younger girls picking peas. And it's hot outside. It's supposed to get up to ninety degrees today."

"Well, don't complain," replied Marilyn. "If I was Twila, I'd much rather pick peas than have a sprained ankle. Anyway, I don't have to leave for a couple of hours yet, so I can help you until then."

It wasn't long until the girls and Mother had picked a bucket of peas. Now that there were peas to shell, Mother said the younger girls could help Twila shell them. The girls sat in lawn chairs under the trees and got started. Robbie sat in his own little chair with a small bowl, determined to help. He stuck diligently to his job for a while, but then wandered off to play in the sandbox.

The girls were hot and irritable and kept arguing with each other. Marilyn finished picking another row of peas and came to join the girls under the trees. Mother said she would finish picking the last row of peas herself. Twila was glad for Marilyn's cheerful presence, and soon all the girls except Suzanne were laughing and talking happily. Suzanne refused to join in. She sat dutifully shelling peas and trying to look mature and grown-up.

When Connie and Rita had another giggling fit, Suzanne burst out, "Can't you girls quit laughing? It just grates on my nerves!"

"Well, Suzanne," said Marilyn heartlessly, "I hope your nerves are in shreds by the time we're done shelling peas!"

Suzanne glared at her but said nothing. Twila suggested, "Why don't we recite all the poems we can think of that we learned in school?" This proved to be a welcome diversion from the tediousness of shelling peas. Together the girls recited "A Leak in the Dike," "Faithful Jim," "Once There Was a Puppy," "A Psalm of Life," and "The Old Violin." They kept on until they couldn't remember any more, and then they started singing school songs.

Mother brought in the last bucket of peas from the pea patch and then went in to get Tanisha. When Mother couldn't keep a close eye on Tanisha, she required her to stay in her room where the alarm was. But she liked to keep Tanisha with the rest of them as much as possible. She settled Tanisha into a chair and showed her how to shell peas. She gave her a little bowl and then took a bigger bowl and started shelling peas herself.

Twila watched Tanisha closely. Would Tanisha obey Mother, or would she throw a screaming fit as she often had in the past when Mother told her to do something?

Tanisha sat still for a long time and then slowly started shelling peas, her face blank. Twila wondered, as she often did, what Tanisha was thinking.

Two days later, the weather was still hot and sticky, and Twila plopped down on the couch. Her ankle was almost totally better, but the heat left her feeling wilted. At her own special sitting spot in the living room, Tanisha sat quietly playing with Lego blocks. Mother folded up a magazine she'd been reading and commented, "Well, Tanisha, you sat there playing quietly for five minutes. Come to the table, and you may have a cookie. Twila, go call the other children. They'll want one too."

Twila called the other children, and they promptly came running, delighted at the prospect of a rare treat. Mother set the container of cookies on the dining room table, but Tanisha went and sat down at the kitchen table.

"No, Tanisha," said Mother. "Come sit at the dining room table." Tanisha got up and came out to the dining room table, but she just stood there. "Tanisha, sit down," said Mother. Tanisha slowly sat down on the edge of a chair.

She sure doesn't miss an opportunity to do things differently than what Mother tells her, Twila thought irritably. While the other children happily ate their cookies, Tanisha nibbled on hers with a pained expression.

"Mother!" exclaimed Suzanne. "May we set up the sprinkler and have a water fight? It's so-o-o-o hot out!"

"And remember," added Rita hopefully, "Miss Patty said we're supposed to go out of our way to have fun."

"Yes, Mother," chimed in Connie. "We always laugh a lot when we have water fights."

"Oh, you do, do you?" Mother laughed. "So you think water fights is what Miss Patty had in mind?"

"Oh, yes!" assured Suzanne. "Water fights and all that kind of stuff."

"Well, it *is* warm," said Mother. "And I don't mind if you play in the water. But listen," she added before the girls could cheer. "You keep the water mess outside. And stay outside until you're ready to put on dry clothes. I don't want you coming in and out of the house with wet clothes. Maybe after a bit I'll bring Tanisha out and let her run through the sprinkler."

Squealing and laughing, the three middle sisters ran out of the house with Robbie on their heels. He was cheering too, though he didn't really know what they were so excited about. The girls filled up several buckets with water to throw at each other before attaching the water hose to the sprinkler.

Twila put the cookies away and Mother wiped off the table before taking Tanisha out to join the other children. They were already laughing their delight as they ran through the cold water. "You need to come too, Twila," shouted Connie. "It feels *so* good!"

Mother took Tanisha's hand and tried to run with her through the mist of cold water. But Tanisha ran stiff-legged beside her with that familiar blank expression.

Twila was suddenly furious. Why couldn't Tanisha ever act nice? She snatched up one of the buckets of water sitting nearby and impulsively dumped it over Tanisha's head. As the water splashed down over her, Tanisha sucked in her breath and gave several gasps. Then to the amazement of them all, she laughed—a sweet, childish, normal laugh, not the mean, hollow laugh she gave when she hurt someone, but a beautiful, happy laugh!

"Whoopee! She laughed! She actually laughed!" shouted Suzanne. And then remembering that she was to keep her praise of Tanisha low-key, she clapped her hand over her mouth.

Twila felt half guilty for getting so upset and pouring the bucket of water over Tanisha. But even more, she felt elated. Tanisha had laughed! Tears of sudden joy sprang into her eyes. Not wanting anyone to see her tears, she ran into the sprinkler and let the water rain down over her face.

She had laughed! Tanisha had laughed!

CHAPTER TWELVE

Dollhouse Trauma

Warm July days followed each other and now August was here. July, for the most part, had been a happy month. Tanisha was responding well to the structured home environment Dad and Mother had carefully established. But more than that, the family had learned that it was possible to be at peace, even with a perpetually brewing storm in the house. They were learning they could still find happiness, even on the days Tanisha seemed determined to destroy it. And she was improving, one baby step at a time.

The girls applauded each minute Tanisha was able to play quietly without throwing a screaming fit. They rejoiced in her neatly colored pictures, so different from the scribbled, sloppy ones she had often done at first. The day she voluntarily said "thank you" was cause for celebration. But the changes that meant the most were the times when she sat nicely on Mother's lap. Or the days she obeyed promptly and said, "Yes, Mother," when she was given a command. Though they were delighted with her tiny improvements, the family learned quickly not to overwhelm the little girl with praise. They knew all too well what happened when they did.

"You know," said Suzanne one day, "I was wishing for some excitement before Tanisha came. At first it made me just plain mad the way Tanisha came in here and tried to control everything, but now I'm starting to like her. It's fun watching her get better."

"It *is* rewarding to watch Tanisha overcome her fears," agreed Mother. "It's thrilling to see what God is doing in her little heart!"

"I didn't understand what Miss Patty meant when she said she liked being a therapist for RAD children," Twila said thoughtfully. "But now that we've seen some changes in Tanisha, I'm beginning to understand. She's right. There's something satisfying about helping a hurting child get better."

"There's one thing we need to remember, girls," cautioned Mother. "It's hard for us to break wrong habits, and even harder for Tanisha. This is especially difficult when these habits have been formed because of neglect and trauma. There will be times when she'll go backward rather than forward."

Suzanne grinned and chanted, "One step forward and two steps backward." She looked at the others, "Remember how Great-Aunt Grace used to say that?"

Mother smiled and nodded. "It must have been something they used to chant when she was a child. Even after she got Alzheimer's and lost her mind, she would still say that whenever she was going about the house with her walker. And yes, from what I understand, that's probably what it will be like for Tanisha sometimes. 'One step forward and two steps backward.' But hopefully the time will come when she takes more steps forward than she does backward."

On Thursdays Mother often went to town to buy groceries for the week. She had gotten into the practice of taking one of the children with her each time. Since Tanisha had come, there was little of Mother's time to go around, and this was one way each of the children could have special time with Mother. All of them eagerly looked forward to their turn. Dad planned his work so he could either be at home on Thursdays or take Tanisha with him for a few hours.

Today it was Robbie's turn to go with Mother, and he was brimming with excitement. Mother had promised him that, before coming home, they would go to the park and he could play. "I'm going to ride on the merry-go-round and get dizzy!" he informed the girls.

"Why do you want to get dizzy?" wondered Rita. "I don't like merry-go-rounds. They make me sick!"

But Robbie only replied, "I like to get dizzy!"

"Well, I know one thing!" announced Marilyn. "We're going to clean up this house while Mother's gone. It's a wreck! We've been so busy lately it hasn't gotten cleaned properly in weeks. It was terribly disappointing when Tanisha ruined all those plants in the greenhouse, but I honestly don't see how we could have ever kept up with a produce garden on top of everything else. Now, Suzanne, why don't you and Rita and Connie go clean your room and make the beds? I'll vacuum the floor for you. Twila, if you do the breakfast dishes, I'll start cleaning up clutter. I'm going to clean the light in the living room too. I was so embarrassed the other day when Miss Patty was here. There are spiderwebs on it. I sure hope she never noticed!"

"All right," agreed Twila rather reluctantly. She really wasn't in the mood to clean house, but Marilyn's enthusiasm was catching.

The younger girls weren't so easily persuaded. Connie argued, "Why do we have to have the house so clean? It's not like Queen Elizabeth is coming or something!" Twila grinned. She knew Connie had recently read a biography about Queen Elizabeth. She wanted to side with Connie. But knowing Marilyn would be disappointed, she kept quiet.

Suzanne and Rita heartily agreed with Connie and had no compunction about saying so. "Yes, Marilyn," said Rita. "It's not a bit necessary to do all this cleaning in the middle of the week. We can wait until Saturday like we usually do."

"If you girls help with the work, when we're all done, I'll have a surprise for you!" Marilyn coaxed.

"Well, all right," said Suzanne grudgingly. "But it'd better be good."

Mother gathered up her purse and the van keys. "It's wonderful if you want to clean the house while I'm gone, Marilyn, but just don't get everyone irritated and upset with each other because you're trying to get a bunch of work out of them," Mother cautioned. "It's important to have a clean house, but not that important. And remember," she added with a twinkle in her eye, "the Bible says that even king's houses have spiders."

Twila was surprised. "Does it actually say that?"

"Sure," said Mother. "Go look up Proverbs 30:28." And with that she bid them a cheerful goodbye and went out the door with Robbie bouncing along beside her.

"I never heard of that verse before," said Marilyn. "I'm going to look it up right now." She got her Bible and brought it out to the kitchen and read it aloud to the girls. "The spider taketh hold with her hands, and is in kings' palaces."

Suzanne grinned. "Well, you can cross the light off your list, Marilyn. Having spiders in the house is Biblical, so you won't need to clean it after all."

"Just because there are spiders in kings' palaces doesn't mean we have to leave spiderwebs in our house," retorted Marilyn. "That light is getting cleaned."

The girls fell to work and got a lot accomplished in a short amount of time. Twila finished her dishes and then took a dusting cloth and went to clean her and Marilyn's bedroom.

When the house was cleaned to Marilyn's satisfaction, she got out the blender and made fruit slush for everyone to drink. She filled five tall glasses and put a straw in each one. The girls took them out under the shade of the trees, and while they sipped the cold drink, Marilyn read from a new book Mother had recently bought. Twila wondered if the surprise was exciting enough for Suzanne, but if she didn't like it, she didn't complain.

That evening after supper, the Hammond family lingered around the table talking about the events of the day.

"Jonny Weber gave his notice today that he's going to quit work," commented Dad. "He's going to Central America to teach school. I'm glad he has the opportunity to go, and I wish him the Lord's blessing. But he was one of my most dependable workers on the carpentry crew, and we'll definitely miss him."

"What will you do?" wondered Mother. "Hire someone else?"

"Well, Uncle Tim mentioned to me once that if I ever needed anyone, Jeff would like to learn some carpentry. I thought I'd check and see if Jeff is still interested."

"Jeff wants to do construction work?" asked Marilyn in surprise. "I thought it was Steve who liked that kind of thing. Remember that saber saw Uncle Jerry gave Steve? Well, Steve told me one summer he made twenty birdhouses with it."

Dad shrugged. "I don't know. I'm just going by what Uncle Tim told me."

"On the way home from town today," remarked Mother, changing the subject, "I noticed an ambulance was in at the Hendricks'. I wonder if George had another spell with his heart."

"No," said Dad. "I met their son Frank in the building supply store this afternoon, and he said that Ethel had a bad fall. They were afraid she'd broken a hip, but it turns out she was just badly bruised."

"What do ambulance people do, anyway?" wondered Rita.

"Why, they try to salvage people!" Connie exclaimed. She looked confused at the laughter that rippled around the table.

"I think you meant *save*, Connie, instead of *salvage*. You just got your words mixed up a little," Dad said, and then turned to Rita.

"Connie's right. The EMTs who work on the ambulance crew are trained to help save lives."

"This Saturday is the adoption picnic," Marilyn remembered. "Are we planning to go?"

Dad looked around the table. "Mother and I talked about it, and we think the younger ones should be able to handle the day if we don't make it too long. We think it would be good for all of us to have the opportunity to socialize with other adoptive families. So if you girls want to go, we will." At the girls' enthusiastic response, Dad added, "Well, I guess we'll plan on going then."

The conversation was interrupted by a knock at the door, and Dad got up to answer it. "Hello, Bob!" he greeted. "Good to see you! It's been awhile."

"Just leave the dishes for now and come outside," Mother said quietly as she got up from the table. "You know how they like to see all of you, and Mrs. Graham will probably want to go around and look at the flowers and garden."

They went outside and the Grahams greeted them. "I brought a bird feeder over for you," said Mr. Graham. "You mentioned, Mary Ann, that the squirrels got into your other feeder, so I made this one squirrel-proof. And here's a small candy bar for each of you girls."

The Grahams often popped in for a few minutes when they were strolling the woods trails and, often as not, they brought some small gift along for the girls or Mother. Since Mother and Dad had asked them not to give gifts to Tanisha without their consent, they had always carefully respected their wishes.

Mr. Graham turned hopefully to Tanisha. "Ask your mother if you may have a piece of candy." Tanisha only looked down at her feet and refused to say anything. She still didn't like to ask Mother for anything. Mr. Graham looked disappointed. "Maybe next time you'll be brave enough to ask your mother," he said gently. He gave the other girls their candy and said nothing more to Tanisha.

Mother, Mrs. Graham, and the younger girls went to look at Mother's impatiens, which were blooming beautifully on the north side of the house. Mrs. Graham led the way in her power wheelchair. Twila was about to follow, but she paused when she heard Dad say, "We really appreciate how supportive you are of our methods of helping Tanisha. Would you mind telling me why it's so important to you to encourage Tanisha to have a healthy relationship with my wife?"

Mr. Graham looked thoughtful. "I suppose it's because seeing Tanisha has helped me to really understand my Nancy for the first time. Oh, Nancy's childhood was not as bad as Tanisha's. She had a grandma who cared about her, but although she was never mistreated and her physical needs were always met, her parents never paid much attention to her. I think that's why she turned to nature and humanism. It was to fill a deep void in her life. If she would have had someone to love her like you love Tanisha, she would have grieved, years ago, when our baby died, and she wouldn't have been so bitter and angry when she lost her leg. Since we've met you people, Nancy is slowly learning to love. It's wonderful! But what a lot of time was wasted in the meantime. I guess that's why I want to do what I can to support you in what you're trying to do with Tanisha."

Are those tears in Mr. Graham's eyes? Twila wondered.

Dad's voice was husky as he simply said, "Thank you, Bob!"

In the morning, Mother announced that the peaches they had bought a couple of days before were ready to do up. "We'll can these instead of freezing them like we did the other two bushels." The older girls got out bowls, knives, and peelers, and set to work. Mother sent Connie and Rita downstairs to bring up empty jars, and Suzanne started washing them. They worked steadily all morning and were pleased with what they got done. But after dinner, when energy and enthusiasm were flagging, Mother told the younger girls they could go play.

Suzanne lingered a few minutes, and Twila knew she was afraid that she would miss out on something. They'd had plenty of interesting conversations around the table this summer as they peeled and sliced fruits and vegetables. At eleven, Suzanne often had a hard time deciding which world she wanted to be a part of—the freedom of the younger girls, or the responsibility and good talks of the older girls and Mother.

The steam rose as Marilyn took the lid off the canner. She took the jar lift and carefully placed nine jars in rows on an old towel Mother had placed on the counter. "That makes thirty-six quarts now," Marilyn announced. She put the next group of nine jars into the canner and then came to help Twila peel peaches. As fast as they peeled them, Mother sliced them into jars and poured a light syrup over them.

"Mother, why doesn't Tanisha ever make the alarm in her bedroom go off?" wondered Marilyn. "She was so sneaky and hard to keep track of before Dad put the alarm in. Why isn't she like that now?"

"Don't you remember? She did try out the alarm that one time when she made it go off in the middle of the night," reminded Mother. "I think that was mostly to see if I'd get out of bed in the middle of the night and to find out how promptly I'd be there. But you're right, Marilyn, she hasn't tried it since then. I think that's because she knows the alarm will go off if anyone enters her room, and that helps her to relax and feel safe. That's why an alarm is such an effective tool for children who haven't been used to consistent bedtimes and feeling safe at night."

Twila reached for another peach and began peeling it. She tried to think of a way to ask the question that had lingered in her mind for a long time. At last she spoke. "Mother, do you love Tanisha?"

Mother took from the bowl another peach that Marilyn had just peeled. Her paring knife made quick slices, and chunks of peaches slid rapidly into the jar. She reached for another peach before saying thoughtfully, "I think it's important to remember that love grows. When children come into our home through foster care, we will not instantly love them the same way we do the rest of our family. Also, loving a child who is unable to bond well with their new family is different from loving a child who is able to respond in secure, emotionally healthy ways. If, by love, you mean the good feeling we have when Robbie gives one of us a hug and says cute things then, no, it's not that kind of love."

Mother took the ladle and carefully poured syrup into another jar of fruit before going on. "When Tanisha came into our home, we had to learn how to care for her. We had to discover how to help her feel safe. We needed to learn ways to help her heal from the emotional trauma of her early childhood, and we needed help as a family to know how to respond to her. We got advice on how to relate to Tanisha and talk to her in a language that her hurting heart could understand. We committed ourselves to treating her with love and respect, even when she behaves toward us in very unloving ways.

"In the end, isn't that love? It may not be that warm, good feeling that we feel toward people who love us in return, but in the end, the waters of committed love may run just as deep as the other kind. When we choose to love, the feelings will eventually follow."

"But, Mother, is it worth going to all that work when she may not turn out in the end?" asked Marilyn. "I know that's what some people are saying."

"*Turning out* isn't really a term I like to use," Mother replied. "God is the Judge of hearts, and He only asks us to be faithful to the work He calls us to. It's not up to us to decide whether it's worth it or not. Let me tell you a story to illustrate what I mean.

"When I was a girl, we had a neighbor who lived a very sinful life. As a result, he was often in and out of jail. My dad would regularly visit him, and often as not, Mom would send along some bread or soup for him. When Mr. Ludvik was in jail, Dad liked to visit him two or three times a month. Often he would take some of the other men from church along, and they would have Bible studies with him. They pled with Mr. Ludvik to allow Jesus into his life and explained how God could help him with his problems."

Mother walked over to the sink and got a dishcloth to clean up the table where she was working. "Mr. Ludvik was always willing to listen, but afterward he would shrug his shoulders hopelessly and say, 'But you just don't understand. I never had a mother to love me. There was no one to care about me.' To our knowledge," went on Mother, "Mr. Ludvik never gave his heart to the Lord and as far as we know, he died an unsaved man.

"So, were all the hours my parents invested in him wasted?" Mother looked up at her two oldest daughters. "I don't think so. Their example taught my brothers and me a valuable lesson. Each soul God puts on earth is worthy of not only our love but also our time. When I get discouraged with working with Tanisha day after day, especially when we see so little result, I often think of my parents and their example. Mr. Ludvik had to choose to allow God into his life, and Tanisha will also have to choose right as she grows up. If she continues rebelling and making wrong choices, she could very well end up in jail someday. But by the grace of God, she will never honestly be able to say, as Mr. Ludvik did, that she had no mother to love and care about her."

Twila set the last empty peach box by the door. "Are we going to adopt Tanisha?" she wondered.

Mother began clearing off the table and setting dishes by the sink to be washed. "Mrs. Gunther called me the other day, and she said they haven't found any relatives who are able to adopt Tanisha. In just a few more weeks, if no one comes forward, we will be free to start adoption procedures if we want to."

"Are you going to?" Marilyn wondered.

Mother was slow to reply. "Dad and I are seriously considering it. What do you girls think we should do?"

Twila had mixed feelings. She had known it could very well come to this, and she wasn't sure how she felt.

Marilyn sighed. "We've put so much into learning about bonding and attachment that it seems a shame to stop now. Besides, what would happen to Tanisha if we didn't adopt her? She's so difficult, she'd probably just drift from one foster home to another, and that would only make her problems worse. But it's scary to think of actually taking her in as a permanent part of our family. As long as we're just doing foster care, we know that if it gets too bad, we can always ask to have her placed somewhere else."

"Well, this is something we want to take plenty of time to think about. Just pray about it, girls. Dad and I need a lot wisdom to make this decision."

Mother glanced at the clock. "It's soon going to be time for me to go get Tanisha from her nap. You girls will need to clean up this kitchen because I should take some time for her. And I'd like to take care of some laundry too."

Marilyn tackled the stack of dishes, and Twila got a bucket of water and started washing the very sticky floor. When Twila was finished, Marilyn suggested, "We ought to wax this floor while we're at it. Mother said it could use a good shine."

Twila hesitated. She had been planning to slip back to the coolness of the woods and read a book for a while. She was ready to escape the heat of the kitchen, not dream up more work to do.

Seeing her reluctance, Marilyn cajoled, "It won't take long and I'll help you. I promise."

"Well, okay!" Twila agreed at last. "But let's do it quickly. I'm tired of working."

They were almost done when Tanisha came into the kitchen. In spite of the heat, she had three blankets wrapped around her— one around her head, one around her shoulders, and the other around her waist. With hands clutching the blankets and a deep scowl on her face, she padded across the freshly waxed floor and leaned her back against the cupboard. She slid down until she was squatting on the floor, with fistfuls of blanket still firmly grasped in her hands.

Twila was indignant, but Marilyn only laughed. "Come on, sweetie!" she coaxed. "You need to get off that floor. We just waxed it."

But Tanisha only stared back, her face set in dark, grumpy lines. It was obvious she had no intention of moving.

Twila concluded there was no sense in getting mad over the situation, so she joined Marilyn in trying to gently tease Tanisha into a better mood. They had no success. Tanisha only looked back at them with brooding eyes. But after much laughing and coaxing, they did eventually get Tanisha to leave the kitchen until the floor was dry. Marilyn tried to smooth over the smudges Tanisha had made, but in spite of her efforts, the marks would be there until the next time they stripped the wax from the floor.

"I don't know why anyone would want three blankets on in this heat," mused Twila. "But it must make her feel safer right now to have them wrapped around her."

Finished with her work, Twila went into the living room to find her book. There was such a nice breeze coming in the windows that she decided to stay in and read rather than going back to the woods. She found a chair and curled up to read. But she didn't get very far.

The rest of the afternoon didn't go well. Tanisha changed from brooding to sassy and disrespectful. Finally Mother sent her back to her room for some quiet time. Mother went to her own room to fold the clean laundry lying on her bed. A short time later, as Mother brought her back out, Twila heard Tanisha say in a bold voice, "That sure was nice having some quiet time. It was fun!"

Mother smiled and said sweetly, "That's wonderful! I enjoyed my quiet time too." She led Tanisha to her sitting spot in the living room and set the dollhouse nearby so she could play with it.

Tanisha piled all the dolls, except for two of them, off to the side. She laid the doll that Marilyn and Twila had always called Grandma on the bed in the bedroom. She stood the dark-haired little girl doll in the bedroom close by the Grandma doll.

Twila watched as Tanisha walked the little girl doll across the room to where the Grandma doll slept. Tanisha made the little girl doll tap the sleeping doll. In a pleading baby voice, Tanisha said, "Auntie, I'm hungry. I want something to eat."

Tanisha changed her voice to the "auntie." She gave a loud snore and then growled, "Be quiet! Leave me alone."

Several more times, the little girl doll tapped Auntie and pleaded for something to eat. But Auntie only snored. Finally Tanisha laid the little girl doll facedown on the floor, and for a long time Tanisha made the dolly cry piteously.

Mesmerized by the scene before her, Twila let her book drop to her lap. Mother was also sitting nearby, and she was watching too. Totally unconscious of anyone else, Tanisha played scene after scene that clearly portrayed the neglect she had experienced as a tiny child. Twila didn't realize she was crying until suddenly she felt tears dripping off her chin.

She couldn't bear to watch any longer. She jumped up, fled out the back door, and sat down on the steps. Propping her arms on her knees, she laid her head down and let the tears pour down her cheeks. How could she ever get angry at Tanisha when she had gone through so much? Life was so unfair. Why did Tanisha have to face so much neglect and cruelty when she, Twila, had been so blessed?

There were so many neglected, abused children in the world. Suddenly, Twila's tears weren't just for Tanisha. She wept for all the children whose hearts had been broken by a wicked, uncaring world. She cried because she knew there was no way her family could reach all of them. She cried because there were so few people willing to reach out and love these precious children.

Robbie came up to Twila, a look of consternation on his face. He pulled on her arm. "Twila, why you cryin'?" he wondered. Twila looked up. How could she possibly explain to a three-year-old what she was crying about?

She pulled him onto her lap and gave him a hug. "Twila just feels sad right now."

Robbie squirmed out of her arms and said, "I'll get something for your nose." He came back with one small square of tissue. Twila took the small piece gratefully and wiped her dripping nose. But Robbie commanded, "Blow!"

Twila cautiously blew her nose, knowing the tiny tissue would be used up very fast. When she was done, Robbie took the used tissue and said, "I'll frow it in the trash." Taking it in his fingertips, he carried it into the house.

When he came back out of the house, Twila pulled Robbie back into her arms, half laughing and half crying. "What would we do without you, Robbie?"

On Saturday morning, an excited air pervaded the Hammond household as they got ready to go to the adoption picnic. After the events of the day before, Twila felt emotionally exhausted. But the enthusiasm of the rest of the family was contagious, and she soon felt her own excitement growing. They had an hour's drive to the park where the adoption picnic would be held. The miles flew by. The rest of the family chattered around her, but Twila sat with her chin propped in her hand, gazing out the window. On a bank overlooking the road, sumac flamed a brilliant red. In a few more weeks, the maples would be giving their once-a-year show of red, yellow, and orange. Twila loved fall.

It didn't seem long until they were pulling into Oakwood Park. Suddenly Twila felt nervous. Already vehicles were lined up in the parking lot. All kinds of people attended this picnic, but as she scanned the faces of those already there, she recognized only a few.

Though the others were nervous, Robbie and Suzanne weren't afraid. Suzanne took her little brother by the hand and led him to a crowd of other children playing on the swings and slides. Connie shrank against Twila, and Twila held her hand as they walked to the pavilion where adults and older children were milling about, visiting.

A tall lady detached herself from a group of other women and bustled over to welcome them. "My name is Rebecca, and I'm Mrs. Daniel Burkholder. I'm so glad you could come today!" She showed Mother a table where she could place the tray of vegetables she'd brought along and introduced her to some other ladies standing nearby. Rebecca took Twila and Marilyn over and introduced them to a couple of girls standing on the other side of the pavilion.

With Rebecca's friendliness and warm welcome, Twila found herself relaxing. Connie apparently felt the same way, because when two girls about her age came up and suggested they play on the swings, Connie went with them.

After Connie left, the two older girls introduced themselves to Marilyn and Twila. "I'm Candace," said the blonde girl. "I'm fifteen and I have three brothers. That's Dominic sitting over there by my mom, and the other two are out there swinging on the monkey bars." Twila tried to follow the girl's pointing finger. She found the little brother sitting by his mother. But there were so many children playing on the gym set that she wasn't sure who was who.

The shorter, dark-haired girl said her name was Irene, and she was fourteen years old. She jiggled a little boy on her hip. Twila's fingers itched to touch his head full of dark kinks, but she kept her hand down. "Is this your little brother? How old is he?" she asked.

Irene shifted the boy in her arms and replied proudly, "Yes, he's legally and officially my little brother! His adoption was finalized last month, just one day before his first birthday."

As the other girls visited and got to know each other, Twila fell silent and listened to the flow of conversations around them. Much of the talk centered on adoption. The women talked about future adoption plans or marveled over God's leading in past placements. One lady was giving a new mom tips on the hair and skin care of her chubby brown-skinned baby. Two men nearby were discussing the financial aspects of adoption.

Somehow Twila's eyes kept drifting over to Candace's little brother sitting beside his mother. He was smiling and chattering freely with a lady sitting nearby and seemed to have totally charmed her. It was a phony charm that Twila recognized, and a feeling of annoyance swept through her. She could easily guess what his behavior was like at home. A moment later, Twila glanced back to see Dominic's mother pulling a box of crayons and a sheet of paper out of her handbag. She gave the paper and a crayon to the small boy, and he started to color.

A freckle-faced girl who looked about ten walked over to where Tanisha and Mother were sitting. "Do you want to come play on the merry-go-round? I'll push you."

Tanisha didn't say anything. She knew she wasn't allowed to go without permission, and she didn't want to ask Mother if she could go. Mother smiled at the girl. "Thank you, but Tanisha will just stay with me."

The girl's mother tried to be helpful. "Oh, you can trust your little girl with Heather. She's good with children, and she'll be careful."

Mother said kindly, but with a note of firmness, "It's best if Tanisha stays with me."

The smiles faded from the faces of mother and daughter, and there was a moment of awkwardness before the conversation resumed.

Irene had also overhead the conversation, and she looked at Marilyn and Twila, puzzled. "Why doesn't your mother let her play with my sister?" she asked almost accusingly.

Twila was silent. She hoped Marilyn would have an answer to this difficult question. At last Marilyn spoke slowly. "Have you ever heard of attachment disorder?" When Irene shook her head, Marilyn continued, "It's what can happen when a child experiences neglect and mistreatment at a very young age. This makes it difficult to bond to their parents, especially the mother. They don't feel safe unless they're close by their mother. Until Tanisha feels secure with our mother, our parents believe it's best to limit her interaction with other people."

Irene looked skeptical. "How do you expect an adopted child to be normal if you don't let her play with other children?"

Candace spoke up this time, and Twila noticed the pain that

was hidden in the back of her eyes. "Some things are just hard to understand. Sometimes it's better to pray than criticize."

Irene looked rather taken back. "I wasn't trying to criticize! It's just that I don't understand why anyone would keep a child from playing with the other children. My parents are never that strict with us."

In the uneasy silence that followed, none of the girls knew quite what to say. They were all relieved when Daniel Burkholder called for everyone to gather around for prayer before they ate.

The day passed quickly, and at three o'clock, Dad said it was time to go home. As they traveled, the younger girls chattered excitedly about the day. "That was fun, Dad!" said Connie. "I talked to a girl who was from Mexico just like me. Can we go again next year? I'd like to see her again."

"Well, we don't know what we'll be doing a year from now, but if we can make it work, I'm sure we'll go," Dad replied.

Robbie and Tanisha had both fallen asleep, and the rest of the girls had fallen silent when Mother glanced back at Twila. "Well, Twila! We haven't heard much from you. How did you enjoy the day?"

"It was kind of scary at first, meeting all those new people, but I'm glad we went," Twila responded. "I saw you talking to Candace's mother, the one with the little boy named Dominic. Does he have RAD too? He reminded me so much of..." Twila let her voice trail off, and the others knew she meant Tanisha.

"Yes, Dominic does have attachment disorder," replied Mother. "It's a very sad situation, and I don't want to betray any confidences. We need to remember to pray for Dominic and his family."

"That's too bad," said Marilyn. "I can sure sympathize with them. We know how difficult it can be. Mother, did you know that their last name is Weber, and they're related to the Webers in our church?"

Mother nodded. "Yes, I found that out today. I wouldn't have known that before."

"I hope sometime they visit in our area and come to see us too," said Twila. "I really liked Candace."

The following week was a busy one, and when the phone rang for the second time in one day, Mother hung up the phone with a troubled air. At the girls' questioning looks she replied, "That was Ethel Hendricks. She was wondering if we could clean her windows sometime this week. We also have church cleaning Thursday evening, plus Marilyn has her usual afternoon of cleaning at Mrs. Graham's. We may just have to say no to some of these things."

"But, Mother," protested Marilyn, "I thought you and Dad always put a high priority on church work. And you always tell us that helping our neighbors is a good way to be a witness to them."

"I know," Mother agreed. "That's how Dad and I have always felt, but since Tanisha has come, we've had to reshuffle our priorities. Right now, God has placed Tanisha with us, and she has many needs. We can't let even good things distract us from the work God has called us to do right now. But I didn't tell Mrs. Hendricks that we couldn't come. I told her I'd call her back and let her know if it would suit. I want to talk to Dad about it this evening. He may have some ideas how we can make this work."

In the end, Marilyn went to Mrs. Graham's for just an hour to help her with some essentials rather than staying several hours as she usually did. Marilyn, Twila, and Suzanne went to the church cleaning. Dad and Mother stayed home so Tanisha could have a quiet evening with them. But on Saturday afternoon, Dad stayed home with Robbie and the younger girls while Mother, Marilyn, Twila, and Suzanne went to the Hendricks' place to help them clean their windows. They worked their way around the house, with Twila washing the higher windows and Mother doing the basement windows on the ground level. With four of them working, the windows didn't take long, and they were home in plenty of time for supper.

CHAPTER THIRTEEN

Birthday Misunderstanding

Summer vacation was slipping away, and in just a few days school would begin. Twila and Marilyn sorted through their newly purchased school supplies lying on the bed. In the closet hung crisp new dresses waiting to be worn on the first day and new school shoes, stiff and never worn. Twila felt excitement course through her. She loved school!

"Which color of mechanical pencil do you want?" wondered Marilyn. She held up two, one pink and the other purple. "I'll take the purple one," Twila replied, knowing that Marilyn preferred pink.

Suzanne entered the room and announced, "When you're done here, Mother wants you girls to come and get things ready to butcher chickens at Uncle Tim's tomorrow."

Twila turned up her nose. "I don't like butchering anything, especially not chickens. But I suppose it won't be too bad since we can do it at Uncle Tim's place."

"I don't mind butchering chickens," replied Marilyn. "It sure was nice of Aunt Carol to raise them for us this year. She raised some for her married daughters and Grandma Hammond, so they're going to be there too. I think it'll be fun!"

"Well, I hope Carla brings her two little children then." Twila grinned. "Maybe I can babysit instead of helping butcher!" She stuffed the last of her school things into her book bag.

Suzanne shrugged. "You can babysit. I don't care! I plan to help the boys catch chickens and chop their heads off."

She laughed when Twila shivered and exclaimed, "I don't see how you can stand it!"

The girls went out to the garage and collected coolers, big bowls, knives, and everything else Mother thought they'd need, and loaded them in the van.

"I'd like to leave at six tomorrow morning," Mother said. "We'll pick up Grandma Hammond and drop Tanisha off with a respite care family on our way."

"Why don't you just let someone in our church babysit Tanisha?" wondered Marilyn. "Why are we taking her to stay with someone we don't know?"

"This couple who does respite care have been trained to provide care for children with attachment disorder. They understand how to ignore Tanisha's fake charm and support us in working with Tanisha's problems. Sometimes it helps when someone besides Mom and Dad encourage a child to change their poor behaviors. Knowing Tanisha is with caregivers who are knowledgeable about her problems gives us a break and a chance to relax. We would be glad if someone in our church would be willing to learn how to do respite care for Tanisha. Uncle Jerry and Aunt Julia know how, but they have their own little crew of children, so they won't be able to take Tanisha very often."

Mother and the girls climbed into the van early the next morning, some of them still rather groggy with sleep. Tanisha walked beside Mother, her shoelaces trailing along the ground. She was supposed to ask Mother for help with anything she couldn't do herself, but she still didn't often ask Mother for assistance with anything. At the van door, Mother bent down and tied her shoes for her.

Tanisha gave a triumphant smile. "You tied my shoes, and I never even asked you to."

Mother gave the little girl a quick hug and smiled gently down at her. "You know you're supposed to ask me for help, but I know it's hard for you to ask. So this time, I just did it for you."

The gleam in Tanisha's eyes faded, and she pulled away from Mother with a frown. Quickly, she climbed into the van and buckled herself into her car seat before anyone could do it for her.

In due time Grandma Hammond was picked up, Tanisha was dropped off, and they arrived at Uncle Tim's.

Cousins Jeff and Steve, along with the help of their younger brothers, dutifully began the job of lopping the heads from the hens. "But as soon as this job is done," Steve announced emphatically, "we boys have better things to do!"

As Suzanne had hoped, she was allowed to help the younger boys catch chickens. The women and girls set up tables not far from the chicken house. As fast as the boys had the birds slaughtered, the ladies began to butcher them.

As Twila had hoped, Uncle Tim and Aunt Carol's married daughters, Rose and Carla, had come to help. But Carla's babies were playing contentedly on a blanket nearby and didn't need her to babysit, so Twila reluctantly picked up a knife and began helping dress chickens. The morning passed by with laughter and chatter among the women and girls as they worked.

Suzanne came to the door of the chicken house, holding a flapping chicken by the legs. "Here, take it," she told Benny. "I'm going to go in and get the last two chickens."

Her cousin shrank back from the chicken's wildly flailing wings and refused to take it. Suzanne's eyes flashed indignantly. "You are too taking this chicken!" she commanded. "If you don't, I'll . . . I'll chase you with it!"

Benny gave one desperate glance around and took off running around the chicken house. Impulsively, Suzanne flew after him, the chicken still firmly in her grasp.

Mother gasped and scolded, "Suzanne!"

But Suzanne didn't hear, and Aunt Carol chuckled heartily. "Just let them be. They'll work it out in their own way. It doesn't hurt Benny to toughen up a little."

Not long afterward, Benny and Suzanne came giggling around the other side of the chicken house with no apparent hard feelings between them, each carrying one leg of the wilted, limp-looking chicken.

Cousin Rose had been married only a few months. She and her husband had hosted overnight visitors for the first time since their marriage. As Rose shared her struggles of cooking for her guests, Twila laughed along with the others. "The meat was overcooked and dry, and the mashed potatoes were lumpy," Rose said. "I was so glad that the next morning I wouldn't have to cook anything. I was just going to serve cold cereal and fresh fruit. But then my husband told our company that I make good breakfasts! So I felt obligated to make pancakes and scrambled eggs instead," she concluded with an aggrieved air. Grandma chuckled and comforted Rose with stories of her own cooking failures through the years.

Since Tanisha had come, Twila realized more what a blessing it was to experience family love and emotional health. It was so healing to be with her Hammond relatives and allow the genial conversation to flow around her.

After that, the conversation turned to more serious topics. Aunt Carol spoke as she dropped another chicken into a tub of cold water. "I think I owe you an apology, Mary Ann, for my criticism of your methods with Tanisha. Tim suggested I go to the library and find a book on reactive attachment disorder. He thought maybe that would help us understand better what you're dealing with. That book explained the effects that early childhood neglect and trauma have on children. It gave a lot of information.

I still don't understand it very well, but I think it's a little clearer in my mind than before, what you face with Tanisha."

Mother nodded. "It's a big subject. It's hard to describe in a fifteen-minute conversation how this disorder affects children's behavior and how best to treat it. But I'm sorry I didn't explain it in a way you could understand."

"From what I read," went on Aunt Carol, "children can have even more emotional damage when they're neglected than when they're abused. Is that true?" she asked skeptically.

Mother zipped shut another bag of meat and placed it in the cooler. "Yes, that's what Alex and I are learning from the therapist. I think it's because a neglected child doesn't remember any abusive incidents that you can refer to when you want to help her understand what happened and work through the reactive emotions. There's just a nothingness there. Oddly enough, children usually prefer the wrong kind of attention than none at all. But saying that doesn't minimize the tragic results when a child is physically abused."

A silence settled around the group as they pondered this thought.

"You know," said Carla, "I was skimming through that book Mom had. I read one place that a child can be affected by things that happened even before they can remember. How is that possible?"

"Well," said Mother thoughtfully, "maybe this would explain how that can happen. When Marilyn was a newborn, I was a new mom and rather awkward at bathing her. One time when she was just a few weeks old, I accidentally got water in her face. She gasped and choked and then started screaming in terror. For months after that, she hated to have a bath. Even just the sound of water running or splashing would cause her to start crying. There was no way she could remember having water splashed in her face that long afterward, but somehow her reflexes were programmed to remember the fear."

Understanding dawned on Rose's face. "That makes sense to me! I could never understand why I'm so afraid of an ambulance siren, even now that I'm older. But now I think I know why. Remember, Mom, how you told me that I got pneumonia when I was three weeks old and had to go the hospital in an ambulance? You weren't allowed to ride along, so you and Dad followed behind. To this day, whenever I hear an ambulance, I tense up and my heart just starts pounding. I know it's ridiculous to be scared like that, but I can never reason myself out of it. Apparently I'm still reacting to what happened back then, even though I can't remember it."

"I'm sure you're right," agreed Mother. "But you were raised in a loving home, so the only negative effects you have from that experience is a pounding heart whenever you hear a siren. But when a child faces negative experiences over and over again and has no caring adult to help him make sense out of what has happened, these things can have a drastic effect on his or her emotional health."

Rose said soberly, "We just can't be thankful enough for all the blessings we receive from being raised in a Christian home!"

"So, is Tanisha a lot better now that you have her in therapy?" wondered Carla.

"Yes and no," replied Mother. "She's made progress, and we're very pleased. But it only comes in very small steps, and she often regresses. The emotional reactions she learned while being so neglected as a small child are not going to disappear overnight. It will likely take months—maybe even years—for her to heal. Even so, I expect that she may carry some of the effects of her childhood trauma all through life. God heals in different ways, and we'll just have to wait and see how He chooses to work in

Tanisha's life. It will also depend on the choices Tanisha makes as she grows older. Please keep praying for us! Alex and I need daily wisdom to know how to help her."

Aunt Carol looked dismayed. "You mean this isn't something she'll get over in just a few months?"

Mother shook her head slowly. "No, I'm afraid not, unless God sends a miracle. The emotional damage that comes with neglect runs deep and takes a long time to heal."

"You sure must have a special love and compassion in your heart to take on a child with problems like that," said Rose admiringly.

Mother shook her head. "There's nothing special about what we're doing. We just want to serve God as any other Christian does. Alex and I love children, and this is where God has called us. We simply want to be faithful."

At noon everyone stopped to eat lunch and then returned to finish the last of their work. To Twila's delight, she was allowed to rock Carla's chubby baby boy while Carla went to settle her daughter for a nap. She amused him by playing peekaboo and other baby games. He had a low, funny little chuckle that made her laugh just to hear him.

When Carla came back to retrieve her small son, Twila helped finish the dishes and then went outside. The other ladies were packaging up the last of the chicken. Mother and Marilyn were loading their and Grandma's share of meat. Twila grabbed a brush and a rag and started scrubbing an empty table. An hour later, the last of the mess had been cleaned up and put away. Mother, Grandma, and the girls climbed in the van and made their way home.

The following Tuesday, school started. Brenda Ramer, one of the ladies from church, offered to take the girls to and from school for the first half of the school year. "I know you're busy with Tanisha, and I'd like to do more to help. But I'm so busy with my own little people that I don't always get done what I'd like to. It's not much out of my way to pick up your girls, so I'd really like to help you in this way. If it's all right with you!"

Mother had gratefully accepted, so on that first morning, the girls merrily called goodbye to Mother as they dashed out of the house to the waiting vehicle. Robbie's wails followed them out the door. It was hard to be the littlest and left behind. As the van pulled out of the lane and onto the highway, Twila could see Robbie standing at the window waving and crying at the same time.

Those first weeks of school, Tanisha's behavior sharply declined, and Twila was glad Mother didn't have the added responsibility of driving the schoolchildren every day.

What was causing Tanisha's regression? Was it the sudden change to the school schedule? Was it because Jeff had started working for Dad? He stayed at Grandma Hammond's during the week, but several evenings a week he ate with their family. This did not change Tanisha's spot at the table, but it was still a change in their normal routine.

Or was Tanisha's sudden regression because Dad and Mother had made the decision to adopt her? Maybe it had nothing to do with any of these things and would have happened regardless. It was hard to know.

Twila couldn't help shedding some tears over Tanisha's decline. It was so disappointing to see her revert back to her old behaviors again. She found herself tensing as she entered the house each day after school. Although the tightly structured environment Mother and Dad had set kept both Tanisha and the other children safe, she still displayed annoying behaviors that wore away at one's nerves.

Lately Tanisha persisted in making continual nonsense noise. There was no simple way to just make her stop. So Mother and

Dad tried to set up circumstances that would help her to control her mouth.

As the girls walked in the door after school one day, Mother was saying, "Okay, Tanisha, why don't you do thirty jumping jacks? While you do them, you may make all the noise you want."

Tanisha jumped energetically, the whole time making a strange unnatural clamor that was different from the noise most small children make.

"Mother, why does she make all that racket?" complained Suzanne.

"I don't know," said Mother. "Maybe it's a way for her to blank out unwelcome memories that flood into her mind. But maybe there are other reasons. Why don't you ask her yourself and see what she says?"

Suzanne jumped up from the table where she had been eating her after-school snack. "All right! I will!"

"Ask nicely," Mother called after her.

Suzanne went out to the living room where Tanisha was continuing to do jumping jacks long after the required thirty had been finished.

"Tanisha, why do you make that noise over and over again?" Suzanne asked, trying hard to keep the frustration out of her voice.

Tanisha stopped jumping and stood with her feet spread wide apart where she had given her last hop. "I do it because it keeps me safe," she replied. "When I make noise, it scares people away and they can't get me." Twila could see that for once, Tanisha seemed to be speaking honestly of her feelings.

"But you're safe with us!" There was amazement in Suzanne's voice. "And who's going to get you anyway?"

Tanisha just shrugged. She seemed to have only a vague idea of who was going to "get" her.

When they finished their snack, the girls scattered to do their various chores. Twila finished hers and sat down at the dining room table to study for a social studies test. Marilyn came in with an armload of laundry and started folding clothes at the table. As she laid out several socks she couldn't find mates for, she exclaimed, "I'm almost positive our dryer eats socks. Where else could they possibly be?"

Twila looked up from her book. "Probably if you would look behind beds or under couches and chairs, you'd find some," she said.

Mother brought Tanisha into the dining room and asked, "Is there room for Tanisha yet too?"

Marilyn pushed the pile of clothes over and made a spot for the little girl. When Tanisha was seated, Mother placed a pre-school book and a pencil in front of Tanisha and gave her instructions on how to do the next page. "Marilyn, would you mind keeping an eye on her and helping her if she needs it?"

Tanisha ignored her book. Instead, she chattered to Marilyn, proudly telling her all the naughty things she had done that day. She told of how she'd refused to obey Mother and how she had torn a page out of Mother's book when she'd been told to put it in the bookcase. Marilyn listened closely, watching Tanisha's face.

Marilyn folded another pair of Robbie's jeans and laid them on the stack with the others. "You know what I'm noticing?" she asked Tanisha.

Tanisha shrugged. "What?"

"I'm noticing how sad your eyes are. You're telling me all these bad things you did today, and you have the saddest eyes I've ever seen." As Marilyn talked, Tanisha squinted her eyes into smaller and smaller slits so that Marilyn couldn't look into them. "Yes," Marilyn went on. "You weren't being good, and now your eyes are so sad!"

Tanisha looked down at her paper. For a long time she just sat there quietly. Then slowly she picked up her pencil and began working. In a short time, she had completed all the work Mother had instructed her to do. This time she did it right instead of deliberately doing it wrong.

Marilyn scanned down over the paper. "You got every answer right, and you wrote very neatly," Marilyn praised. She tipped up Tanisha's chin with her fingers and went on. "You know what I'm noticing? I'm noticing how happy your eyes are! You obeyed Mother and did your work. Now your eyes are happy. You have happy eyes instead of sad eyes like you had when you were being naughty."

A shy smile softened Tanisha's features, and she allowed Marilyn to hug her. It was true. Her eyes were happy!

Twila bent over her social studies book, tears blurring her eyes. They had all shed a lot of tears over how difficult it was to live with Tanisha. But she had not expected to cry so much over Tanisha's little successes!

That evening Dad and Jeff were late coming home to supper. Twila was relieved when she saw Dad's truck pull in the driveway. True, there had been that little victory in the afternoon with Tanisha, but she was so unpredictable, and things could change so fast. Tanisha usually behaved better when Dad was home. Maybe it was because it was harder to fight against two adults than just one. Tanisha had only slightly more respect for Dad than she did for Mother, but it was enough to make her behavior a little easier to be around.

So far, when Jeff stayed for supper, Tanisha had tried hard to get his attention with sweet, charming behavior. As of yet, she had never showed her true colors in front of him. But except for an occasional *hello* or *excuse me*, Jeff ignored Tanisha.

Dad came into the kitchen and placed his lunch pail and water jug on the table. "Sorry, dear, that we're so late! The owner came out to the house just as we were ready to come home and wanted to discuss another project he wants me to do. That's why we weren't home sooner."

Mother smiled. "Well, we're just having soup, so the food wasn't spoiled by cooking extra long. As soon as you wash up, we can eat."

The family gathered around the table. After prayer there was cheerful chatter as they ate their chicken and barley soup, fresh rolls, dill pickles, and cheese.

Dad reached over to help Robbie spread apple butter on his dinner roll, but Robbie shook his head and said firmly, "I do it myself!" Clumsily but meticulously, Robbie spread the apple butter on his roll with a table knife. When he was finished, he lifted the knife and licked off the last bit of the sweet spread.

"There, you got it!" Dad praised, and then gently pulled the knife from Robbie's fingers. He smiled at the small boy. "We don't lick our knives at the table."

Dad and Jeff were discussing the following days' work when out of the corner of her eye, Twila saw Tanisha deliberately tip her glass in Jeff's direction. At least, Twila was almost certain that Tanisha had done it on purpose. She was so quick that it was hard to be sure.

Jeff suddenly noticed the water flooding across the table toward him. He jumped up and sang out, "Build an ark!"

Everyone laughed at Jeff's response. Marilyn went to the kitchen to get a rag to clean up the mess. Mother set Tanisha's cup to the side, but gave no other acknowledgment to Tanisha's part in the "accident." Seeing she was being ignored, Tanisha sat moodily in her chair.

The following day was Saturday. Grandma had asked if Marilyn, Twila, and their cousin Sue could spend part of the day at her place cleaning out her garden and flower beds and helping her catch up on the projects about the place that old age would not allow her to do.

The girls picked the last of Grandma's tomatoes that she'd been carefully covering each night to protect them from the frost. Then they pulled up the wire tomato cages and the tomato vines. Twila chopped down the cornstalks with a machete, and Sue and Marilyn hauled them away. When everything was cleaned out of the garden, Marilyn got out Grandma's old Snapper and mowed off the spent plants.

The girls pulled up the dried, frost-bitten flowers and raked the leaves from under the maple in Grandma's front yard. By noon, the girls had worked up a real appetite, and Grandma had plenty for them to eat. Nobody ever went hungry at her table! After eating they sat and visited.

During a lull in the conversation, Twila reached for a pie pan full of unshelled beans that was sitting at the far end of the table. "Grandma, every fall you have a pan of beans sitting on your table. What are they for?" wondered Twila.

Grandma took her finger and stirred through the beans. "They're what we call Bertha beans. I think they're dry enough I could probably shell them now. I'm saving them for next year's seed. Years ago when my sister Bertha got married, she started growing these white shell beans. Her husband's family had brought them over from Germany. She saved seed for me and my sisters, and we started to grow them too. Because we got them from Bertha, we always called them Bertha beans. I have no idea what they originally were called."

The girls listened as Grandma went on to tell more family stories, but at last Marilyn stirred herself reluctantly. "We really need to get these dishes done so we can go home and help Mother yet this afternoon."

When they got home, Suzanne met them at the door. "You'll never guess what Tanisha is doing *now*," she told them. "She's sniffing!"

Suzanne tended to be overly dramatic, and neither of her older sisters took her seriously. Marilyn laughed. "Well, I guess that's better than some things she's done."

Suzanne looked close to tears. "But she just *keeps* sniffing! You don't understand!"

"I wouldn't get all worked up over sniffing," Twila remarked.

Rita walked up, and Suzanne turned to her and exclaimed, "You tell them, Rita!"

Rita shifted uncomfortably and said, "Well, she's been sniffing without stopping."

"You told us that before. What's so terrible about that? At least she's not hurting anyone!" Twila said.

Rita twisted the curly hair at the bottom of her braid around her finger and then added, "But she doesn't quit."

Marilyn looked at her younger sisters with eyebrows raised. "What on earth do you girls mean?" Both girls just shrugged.

As they walked away, Suzanne threw over her shoulder, "*You* listen to her and then you'll find out."

The girls did find out very quickly. Tanisha was sniffing with monotonous persistence, and it was true that she never stopped. As the days slipped by, Twila began to feel like it would drive her absolutely crazy. Even Mother looked worn.

Finally even Marilyn, who was usually the most tolerant of the girls, cried out, "Mother, isn't there something you can do to make her stop? I don't think I can stand it one minute more."

Mother shook her head. "I'm just not sure what to do about it. It's not really hurting anyone or anything except our nerves. I'm not sure how to help her behave in a more socially acceptable way." Suddenly her eyes lit up. "I'm going to call Rachel Bender. She's done foster care for years. She might have some advice for me."

Twenty minutes later, Mother returned from her phone call with a twinkle in her eye and a lotion bottle in her hand. Before she had called Rachel, she had put Tanisha in her room. Now she went to get her and brought her out to her special sitting spot in the living room. Tanisha walked beside Mother, sniffing the whole time.

Mother showed Tanisha the bottle of lotion and said, "I noticed, Tanisha, how much you like to sniff. I don't blame you. That supper in the oven sure smells good! I like sniffing it too. Here's something else you can sniff. It's my new bottle of lotion. It smells like roses. If you want to, you can put some on you. When you sniff it, it will remind you of how much Mother loves you!"

Mother handed her the lotion, and Tanisha tentatively took it. Mother gave Twila instructions to tidy up the living room and then left to go check on supper.

While she worked, Twila watched Tanisha out of the corner of her eye. Tanisha took the lid off the bottle and took a few whiffs. But suddenly, her desire to sniff seemed to disappear. Normally, she would have gleefully wasted all of Mother's lotion. But Mother had given her permission to use it, and had even said the smell would be there to remind her of how much she loved her. Twila wasn't surprised when Tanisha screwed the lid back on without using or wasting one drop of it.

Twila finished cleaning up the living room and went to report to Marilyn what she had observed. "Poor little thing!" said Marilyn. "What must it be like to be that afraid of love?"

Twila sympathized too, but she was happier to see that Tanisha had quit sniffing. She would probably start again later, but even just a few minutes' break was wonderful.

September 24 was Twila's fourteenth birthday. Mother had told her she could invite her friend Beth for a sleepover. Twila had hoped they could set up a tent and sleep back in the woods at the picnic area. But now they were experiencing a cold snap; though the days were sunny and beautiful, the nights were chilly and frosty. So the girls kept their plans of eating supper in the woods, but Twila reluctantly gave up her tenting idea.

Beth came home with the Hammonds after school. Twila was excited to be able to spend this time with her friend. Mother had said she didn't need to do her usual after-school work and suggested that Twila and Beth get a fire started back in the woods. That way the fire would be burned down to hot coals by the time Mother wanted to grill chicken for supper.

The girls went to Twila's room so she could put away her school things. As they were coming down the hall, Beth halted at Tanisha's bedroom door. Her eyes drifted up to the alarm over the door. "What's all *that* about?" she asked, looking shocked. "Do you lock Tanisha up in her bedroom?"

Twila's heart sank all the way down to her toes. She and Beth had talked about Tanisha before, and Twila thought Beth had understood. She struggled to explain it now. "No, we don't lock her up. See, look. There's not even a lock on the door! The alarm just lets us know when she comes out and lets her know when we come in. It helps her to feel safe and secure."

"What? How could an alarm on her bedroom door make her feel safe?" Beth looked incredulous.

"Well . . . Tanisha has some fears that normal children don't have," Twila said. She paused, trying to think how to explain further.

But Beth cut in, "Don't you think if you would treat her more like a normal child, she might behave better? I'd have a hard time loving my family if they did this to me!"

Of all the girls in school, Beth was the only one in Twila's grade, and the closest one to her age. They had always been good friends, but now it seemed as if Tanisha was going to spoil their friendship. Anger simmered up inside Twila. Tanisha had taken away so many things, but Twila was determined that she wouldn't take away her best friend as well.

So she tried to brush away the unpleasant conversation. She changed the subject and tried to talk cheerfully about other things. But she could feel Beth's confused disapproval, and her words kept ringing in her ears. *I'd have a hard time loving my family if they did this to me!* They had loved Tanisha the best they knew how, providing her with security as the therapist had recommended. And Tanisha was showing small improvements in her behavior and attitudes. Beth's opinion was unfair!

The rest of the evening was strained and awkward. Even during supper back in the woods, the usual comfortable feeling between Twila and Beth was gone. Twila tried desperately to be kind and polite, but she wondered if the others noticed the aloofness between them. She was so glad that her plans hadn't worked to sleep out in the woods, and that they would be sleeping in the house with Marilyn. Yet she felt devastated and angry that she should even feel that way, especially when she looked across the fire to where Tanisha was sitting, sweet and smiling, beside Mother.

They all sat around the fire visiting and singing, but when the cool night air began to settle in around them, they packed up the remains of their supper and went back to the house. Twila let Beth go to the house with Dad and the rest of the children and lingered behind to help Mother finish cleaning up.

When she was sure the rest were out of earshot, Twila quickly spilled out to Mother what had happened. As she spoke, she tried desperately to hold the tears back.

Mother was silent for so long that Twila wondered if she was going to scold her for complaining. But when Mother spoke, her voice was gentle and encouraging. "I think you did a good job of handling the situation with maturity. It's normal to feel hurt when we're misunderstood, or angry when someone spoils a close friendship. But you were still kind and respectful even when you were disappointed in Beth. Try not to dwell on your own hurt. Think about it from Beth's angle. What would you have thought if you had gone to her house and saw what she did at ours?"

"But why can't people just believe us?" Twila pleaded. "Why is their first impulse to be so suspicious?"

Mother sighed. "I suppose it's human nature. The people in our circles seldom see children with problems like Tanisha's. It shouldn't surprise us that people wonder. They *should* wonder. I don't think I would get too discouraged about your friendship with Beth. Once she's had time to think it through, she may feel differently about it. Just don't let your anger and hurt turn into bitterness," Mother encouraged.

Twila pulled the tablecloth off the picnic table and shook it out before placing it in the wagon on top of the other supper supplies. She sighed. "I don't want to be bitter about it, but it's just so hard. Sometimes I can't help but wish our family could go back to how we were before Tanisha came."

Mother and daughter walked in comfortable silence up to the house, and Twila felt much better about facing the rest of Beth's stay. The next morning went better than she had expected, and at school she and Beth managed to at least be civil to each other.

Several days later, as the girls walked out to the playground at school, Beth said hesitantly, "I've been wanting to talk to you. I told my mom about Tanisha's room and what I said to you. Mom said we don't understand everything, and that it was wrong for me to judge you like that. She said it would be better to pray for your family instead of being critical. I'm sorry. I wish I hadn't said that stuff to you."

Twila felt her heart grow suddenly lighter. "Don't feel bad," she told Beth. "If I wouldn't live with Tanisha and didn't see how she acts firsthand, I would be like you and have a hard time believing the stories about her too. It's hard to understand, especially when we have parents who love us and have taught us about Jesus. It's hard to comprehend what it would be like to live in a home without love or even wanting to act the way Tanisha does."

Beth looked anxious. "So you'll forgive me and not be mad at me for what I said?"

Twila grinned. "Of course I forgive you, and I'm not mad at you either! I was just so scared that we'd never be friends again."

At a call from the field, Twila ran to join her team in playing prisoner's base, feeling better than she had for several days.

CHAPTER FOURTEEN

Too Much Excitement

Rita slapped her card down on the stack and giggled as she looked across the table to Suzanne's disappointed face. Suzanne recovered and grinned good-naturedly. As she quickly laid another card down, she said, "You're getting too good at this game, Rita! You beat me."

It was November 2. One year ago, Connie's and Robbie's adoption had been finalized. The Hammond family celebrated their adoption day with homemade ice cream and a cake Mother had decorated. Mother had also invited Grandma Weatherby to join them for supper. Because of her lame leg, she seldom drove, so Dad picked her up on his way home from work.

After supper Connie requested that they all play Dutch Blitz. Even Robbie joined in. Dad had given him a few cards and helped him lay them out. Robbie soon learned that a cry of "Blitz!" signaled the end of the game. So frequently he would slap down one of his cards on a pile and joyfully yell, "Blitz!" The other players knew not to take his shouts seriously.

Grandma Weatherby sat at the end of the table and watched them play. Though she struggled to keep up with what was happening in this fast action game, she enjoyed watching and cheered for all of them.

Marilyn placed a number ten card and called, "Blitz!" This time it was for real. The girls laughed and talked as they sorted through the cards, counting them to see who had gotten rid of the most cards.

Twila looked across the table to where Connie was teamed up with Suzanne. As usual, Connie's straight black hair had slipped out of her braid and hung in long strands about her face. Her dark eyes danced with the excitement of the game. Twila wondered momentarily how they had ever gotten along before without Connie and Robbie in their family.

They played several more games before it was time for the younger children to go to bed and for Grandma Weatherby to be taken home. Reluctant to go to bed just yet, Twila grabbed a jacket and hopped in the van with Dad and Grandma.

As they drove along, Grandma exclaimed, "Thank you so much for including me tonight. I don't know when I've enjoyed an evening more!"

Dad slowed down to make a left turn. He replied, "You're more than welcome. We were happy to have you come."

Grandma Weatherby ran her fingers over the smooth wood of the cane she always carried with her. "I know I've told you this before, but I want to thank you again for taking in Robbie and Connie and loving them as your own. Under your love and kindness, they've blossomed in ways I would have never thought possible. I'm so grateful to see my grandchildren growing up in a good Christian home."

"Well," said Dad, "thank God, because if we've done anything good with Robbie and Connie, it's because of Him. I hope you know how much Mary Ann and I appreciate your support of our parenting. You've never tried to interfere with how we're raising Robbie and Connie. We're also thankful for how you've taken all of our children into your heart and accepted them as your grandchildren too."

Grandma Weatherby sounded surprised. "Well, of course! Why wouldn't I? You have a wonderful family, and I think of you all as my family." After a moment she chuckled. "I guess I shouldn't be surprised at you for loving Robbie and Connie. Though it's not legally documented, I've adopted all of you as my family."

As Dad pulled up to Grandma Weatherby's house, the three of them shared a laugh together. Twila offered to walk with her to the house, but Grandma insisted it wasn't necessary. Dad waited until she had reached her front door before pulling away. Grandma gave one last wave before entering the house and Twila waved back even though it was dark and Grandma Weatherby couldn't see her.

During the night Twila woke up to a churning stomach. A few moments later she made a dash to the bathroom to empty its contents. She dragged herself back to bed, weak and drenched with perspiration. That was the first of many times more before morning. She had certainly caught the stomach bug going around.

The next morning Twila sat at the kitchen table sipping some apple juice. She felt somewhat better, but she definitely wouldn't be going to school.

Suzanne lined up the lunch boxes on the counter and began packing them. "Don't forget that there's hot lunch today, so you won't need to make sandwiches," Marilyn reminded her.

"Whose turn is it to bring hot lunch? It isn't ours, is it?" Suzanne wondered as she pulled the cupboard door open to look at the schedule taped inside. "It *is* our turn!" she exclaimed in dismay. "Mother, did you know that?"

Mother looked tired. The past week hadn't been easy. The last few days Tanisha had been especially difficult. "I guess you'll have to stay home from school and help me, Marilyn. With the way Tanisha has been lately, there's no way I'll be able to get a hot dish ready by noon without some help. I'm very sorry! If I'd have thought to check the list earlier, I could have made some preparations yesterday. I wouldn't have had to do it all this morning."

Before Marilyn could say anything, the phone rang and she stepped over to answer it. She only talked for a few moments before hanging up. "That was Brother Don," she announced with a smile. "He said Elva asked him to call and tell us we don't need to worry about making hot lunch. He said Elva knows we're busy, so she's going to do it for us today."

"That certainly was thoughtful of her," Mother remarked with a look of relief. Twila set her empty juice glass down and slipped away to the living room couch. So people did still care! So often it seemed like people showed only momentary compassion. Then they went on with their normal ordinary lives and forgot about the difficulties the Hammond family faced day after day.

Twila picked up the throw from the end of the couch and with a sigh lay down, pulling the blanket up to her chin. She dozed off while the other girls ate breakfast and left for school. She slept for an hour before her stomach woke her up to let her know it wasn't accepting the juice she had drunk earlier.

When she came back to the couch again, Mother was sitting in the rocker with Tanisha. Mother laid Tanisha back in her arms so she could look into her face and make eye contact. Twila watched as Mother tickled her and played little games with her. She sang her own made-up songs that playfully let Tanisha know she was loved. "Who loves Tanisha? Mother does! Mother does! Who loves Tanisha...?"

Every so often when Tanisha would make good eye contact, Mother would pop a goldfish cracker into her mouth. Tanisha still didn't laugh and join in the play like Robbie did when Mother played with him. But slowly she was learning to relax and enjoy these times with Mother. Although some days she refused to cooperate, today she surprised them by saying, "Do it again!"

Though Twila could only see the side of Tanisha's face, she marveled at the sweetness and innocence of her countenance during this unguarded moment. So often her face was taut with anger, pain, or fear. She looked so lovable that Twila felt a surge of affection for the little girl. Perhaps someday soon Tanisha would be able to love in return.

By noon Robbie had also come down with the flu, and he was lying on the love seat, restless and miserable. He couldn't eat, but Twila was able to eat a small dipperful of soup.

After lunch was over and Tanisha was tucked in bed for her nap, Mother came out to the living room and sat rocking Robbie.

Twila laid her book on the back of the couch and looked over at Mother. "I was thinking about being sick, and you know what? I can't remember even one time that Tanisha has gotten sick since she's come to our place. Has she, Mother? Or am I just forgetting?"

The chair kept up its steady rhythm as Mother rocked the small boy in her arms. "You're right. She has never gotten sick since she came to us, and I've wondered about that myself. I almost wish she would be sick sometimes. Maybe at a vulnerable time like that, she would be quicker to reach out to me for comfort."

"Well, maybe she has a stronger immune system than the rest of us," said Twila. "I actually think it's kind of nice to be sick once in a while. No work to do, and I can just read or sleep whenever I feel like it."

Mother gently stroked Robbie's thatch of dark hair. "There are times I so wish that I could have been there to do for Tanisha what the adults in her life neglected to do. I wish I could have been there to feed her when she was hungry, comfort her when she was sad, and hold her when she was sick. But there's nothing we can do to change the choices her family made. God has brought her into our lives, and I'm very thankful that we have this opportunity to love her."

"You really feel that way after the way she's treated you and all the horrible things she's done?" wondered Twila.

Mother smiled. "Yes, I do! Isn't it wonderful what God's love can do?"

Twila lay for a long time pondering what Mother had said. Suddenly she had another question. "What do you think Tanisha's birth mom was like? Have you ever heard much about her?"

Mother had been singing softly to Robbie, but she paused. "From what I understand, there is little information about her. I often think of her though. What must the poor lady have experienced to cause her to abandon Tanisha? The cycle of abuse and neglect is such a vicious one. Many times I wish I could have known Tanisha's birth mom. I wish I or someone else could have been a friend to her. Maybe she wouldn't have made the choices she did if she'd have known someone loved her. That's why Dad and I want to help Tanisha as much as we can. Hopefully the lifestyle of Tanisha's family can stop with her. Won't it be wonderful if Tanisha can grow up to live a godly life?"

Compassion for Tanisha's birth mom! This was a new thought for Twila. The Hammond family had done foster care long enough for Twila to know that there were many different reasons why a child needed to be placed into care, but she tended to think of the biological parents as selfish people who should have taken better care of their children. Now Mother's words put the situation in a whole new light. They were hurting people who needed friends. Most of all, these people needed Jesus too.

At last Twila reached for her book and read for a while before taking another nap. She awoke when the school girls came crashing in the door. Mother tried to hush them, but it was already too late. Both Twila and Robbie woke up. Robbie whimpered to be held, so Mother picked him up and carried him out to the kitchen table where the other girls were talking about their day and eating a snack. Anxious to hear news from school and feeling better than she had all day, Twila went out to the kitchen to join the others.

"Mother, I got a 95 percent on my science test today," Connie informed her.

"And I have a social studies test I need to study for tonight," Suzanne added with a wrinkle of her nose. "I have to remember a bunch of dates, and I'm sure I'm going to fail it."

"Well, don't give up before you even do the test," replied Mother. "Remind me after supper, and Dad or I will help you study."

Rita spoke up suddenly. "You know what Ricky told me today? He said that Janice has leprosy . . . or something kind of like leprosy!"

"She does *not* have leprosy!" Suzanne exclaimed indignantly. "It's not even possible."

Marilyn laughed. "Did they put her outside the camp yet?"

"Oh, no, they wouldn't do that." Twila giggled. "They probably make her go around crying, 'Unclean, unclean!' "

Rita looked totally confused. "We don't get leprosy here in the States," Mother explained. "I talked to Aunt Julia yesterday, and she said that Janice has a bad case of impetigo. It's a rash, but it's different from leprosy. In Bible times God instructed that people with leprosy had to live outside the camp of Israel. Wherever they went, they had to cry out, 'Unclean, unclean' so that people would know not to get too near. This kept more people from catching this dreaded disease."

Rita shivered. "Oh, I'm so glad that's not what Janice has!"

Suzanne tossed her head. "I think it's ridiculous the way some people gossip."

Mother reached out to put an arm around Rita. "Ricky and Rita weren't gossiping. They just got a little mixed up, that's all."

By the next morning Mother had come down with the stomach virus. Robbie was as perky as if he had never been sick, but Twila was still feeling rather washed out. Marilyn got breakfast and helped the younger girls with the lunches. Without Mother's help, things did not go as smoothly as they normally did. Brenda Ramer had to wait on the schoolchildren a little when she came to pick them up. Twila stayed home to watch Robbie so Mother could rest. Dad had to buy some painting supplies, so he took Tanisha to town with him.

After the others had all left, Twila washed up the breakfast dishes and swept the kitchen floor with Robbie's help. She was surprised at how just that little bit of work tired her out, and she was more than willing to sit down to play Memory with Robbie. They sat on the floor and carefully laid the cards upside down.

Robbie was still learning, so Twila did not play her hardest. But once when she was too obvious and deliberately didn't pick up the right card, Robbie chose the right card, exclaiming in a condescending tone, "It's not that one! It's this one!"

Except for when it was his turn, Robbie wiggled and squirmed and gave funny hops, kicking his feet in the air behind him while he waited. "Do you ever hold still?" Twila wondered. Robbie shrugged and then forgot about her question as he took his turn. They played several rounds before he tired of the game and went to play with his tractors.

Dad and Tanisha came home and ate lunch with Twila and Robbie. Afterward Dad put Tanisha to bed and then took some fruit juice into the bedroom for Mother before going back to work.

Twila sat down to read some books to Robbie before putting him down for a nap. He had something to say on almost every page. Twila wished he would be quiet and let her read uninterrupted. He pointed to a picture of a boat. "You're too big to fit in that boat," he informed her.

Twila nodded. "Yes, I'm too big!" she agreed.

They finished that book and then went on to the book that told the 23rd Psalm. Robbie was learning it by heart, so Twila read it slowly, letting him fill in as many of the words as he could. At the end of the book the psalm was put to music, and Robbie insisted they sing it. When the song was done, Twila turned to the last page, and Robbie firmly quoted the single word on the page: "Amen!"

Anxious to curl up on the couch with a book, Twila tried to hustle Robbie along. But Robbie was not about to be hurried through his naptime ritual. They went to Robbie's room, but before he would crawl into bed, he asked Twila, "Can you shut the light on for me?"

Sunlight streamed in through the window, but Twila decided not to argue. "Okay, I'll turn the light on for you, but you need to get into bed now."

Finally content, Robbie crawled into his little bed, and Twila tucked his puppy blanket that Grandma Hammond had made up around his shoulders just the way he liked it. She had just gotten him all settled when his arms popped out and he exclaimed, "Oh, I didn't give you a hug!" Twila bent down and hugged the small boy, kissing him on the forehead.

Twila tried to pull his blanket back up, but Robbie wasn't done talking. "Do I 'serve hugs?" he wondered.

Twila tickled him and replied, "Of course you deserve hugs. Lots and lots of them. Everyone does!"

Robbie giggled and settled back into his bed so Twila could tuck him in again. "Sleep good!" she told him.

"Sleep good too," he replied.

Twila flipped off the light switch and slipped from the room, thinking what a funny little brother she had.

November and Thanksgiving slipped by, and then December was upon them with Christmas fast approaching. Marilyn came in one afternoon from the Grahams with a poinsettia in her arms.

"Mrs. Graham sent it over for you, Mother," Marilyn announced as she carefully pulled the wrappings off the plant. "She said she bought it last winter and planted it in her flower bed this spring. This fall she and Mr. Graham dug it up and put it in a pot. She said she always wanted to try planting a poinsettia and see if she could get it to grow well. Isn't it beautiful, Mother?"

"It sure is," Mother agreed. Marilyn placed the poinsettia in the center of the dining room table. The other girls gathered around Mother and admired the plant's lovely red leaves.

"I know Mrs. Graham says she likes wild things better, but she sure has a knack even with domestic flowers," Mother observed.

In the following days, Mother tenderly watered and cared for the plant, and they all enjoyed the burst of color it added to the room.

One evening Rita and Connie both needed some extra drilling on their math facts. So Mother sat Tanisha beside her at the table. She gave her a pencil and paper and turned slightly to give flash cards to the other girls.

Sometime later that evening, Suzanne gave such a cry of dismay that it brought the other girls running. They all stared in disbelief at the riddled poinsettia. Its leaves had been systematically poked full of holes.

Mother shook her head when she saw the sad-looking plant. "I'm sorry, girls," she apologized. "Tanisha must've done it when I was giving Connie and Rita flash cards. She knew how much we all were enjoying this plant. I must've had my head turned just enough that I didn't catch her doing it."

"What am I going to tell Mrs. Graham when I go over there tomorrow?" groaned Marilyn. "I'm sure she'll ask me how the plant is doing."

Mother sighed. "You'll just have to tell her the truth and hope she understands."

As planned, Marilyn went to work at the Grahams the next afternoon. When she came back, Rita wondered if Mrs. Graham had asked about the plant. She had worried over this almost as much as Marilyn, concerned that Mrs. Graham's feelings would be hurt.

"Yes," said Marilyn, "she did ask." Twila wondered about the twinkle that danced in Marilyn's eyes.

"Well, what did she say when you told her what Tanisha did?" demanded Suzanne.

Marilyn laughed. "She just sniffed and said she'd have poked Tanisha full of holes! I thought about telling her, 'Don't think we didn't consider it!' But I didn't suppose that would be a very nice thing to say."

The younger girls giggled freely over Mrs. Graham's unexpected response. Mother chuckled along with them and then said, "Well, at least she wasn't angry with us because her plant got ruined."

As Christmas drew near, Twila's excitement grew, especially when they learned that Grandpa and Grandma Yutzy were planning to come, and Uncle James and Aunt Danette were also bringing their little boys. Twila looked forward to having a houseful of company for Christmas.

She loved Christmas caroling, family gatherings, and everything that went with Christmas. Though this Christmas would be spent mostly with Mother's side of the family, they were planning to make it to the Hammond gathering on New Year's Day. Depending on the weather, there would likely be skating or a sleigh ride for the children and young people that day. When they were tired and cold, they would come in for hot chocolate and Grandma's Christmas cookies—date pinwheels, raisin cookies, peanut brittle, monster cookies, and frosted cutout cookies. Twila could never resist eating the decorated cookies. Though she knew they were dry and she wouldn't really care for them, she could never quite keep from choosing a star or some other shape. But the green cornflake cookies topped with red hot cinnamon candies were Twila's favorite.

Twila wondered how Tanisha would handle company in the house for three days and all the added activity. She never did well with extra excitement and visitors. Twila knew Mother would try to keep things as quiet and normal as possible without letting Tanisha's needs take away from the rest of the family's enjoyment.

Thursday evening the Hammond family piled into the van and drove to the school where the church people would meet to go caroling. As usual Mother stayed home with Tanisha. Twila felt a momentary pang as she thought how seldom their whole family could do things together. But she pushed the thought away. She wasn't going to let it spoil her enjoyment of the evening. Tonight they would be walking the streets of the little town of Kenton and stopping to sing at houses along the way. There was something about walking through the crisp, cold, starlit night that Twila loved.

When they arrived at the school, Twila reached to help Robbie out of the van. He had insisted on coming along, and Mother had reluctantly consented. She had dressed him warmly, and now he looked like a fat little bear. He trotted into the school with the rest of them, his eyes shining at the privilege of coming along.

When the carolers had all arrived, Uncle Loren, who was in charge of the evening, gave final instructions and then led in prayer, asking God's blessing on the evening.

They filed out of the school and walked to the first house, crowding onto the front porch. An elderly man and his wife came to the door and listened while they sang "Joy to the World," "Silent Night," and "Away in a Manger." As Twila sang, she watched as little Kayla, only five years old, tipped her head back and sang with all her might.

She suddenly got a picture of what Tanisha could have been if she hadn't been hurt and damaged by her birth family. Would Tanisha ever get that sweetness and innocence back again? Twila suddenly realized this was why Jesus had come to earth in the first place—to bring healing, deliverance, and liberty, just like it said in the verse Dad had read in devotions.

When they finished singing, the old couple thanked them profusely and insisted they each take a piece of candy from the dish they brought out. Then the group trooped off the porch and went on to the next place. Some places they were welcomed warmly; others less so. Some houses they skipped altogether, having learned from previous years that the occupants didn't wish to be disturbed.

Robbie held Twila's hand and trotted along on sturdy legs. It didn't take him long to learn the songs, and soon he was adding his piping little voice to the rest of the carolers.

The next house was the home of two Catholic nuns. But this year only one of the ladies came to the door. They sang three songs and ended as usual with "We Wish You a Blessed Christmas." Other years, the two ladies would sing back to them their own version of the song. But this year the lady sang alone. Then with well wishes and goodbyes, the group moved on to the next place.

"I wonder where the other lady was?" Twila asked Beth as they walked away from the house.

Beth replied, "I think I heard someone say she died."

"Oh, that's too bad!" Twila exclaimed. "I always liked seeing those two ladies every year."

They had one more place to go, and that was Grandma Weatherby's right beside the school. Rather than stand outside, she insisted they come in the house. Limping, she led the way into the living room and sat down in her chair. Robbie, tuckered out from the evening, sat contentedly on his grandma's lap.

Though they didn't sing with the gusto they had earlier in the evening, the small living room rang with the voices of the singers. Twila's eyes traveled from Grandma Weatherby sitting in her chair to the pictures on the walls. There was one of her son, Connie and Robbie's birth father, when he had graduated from high school. There was a photo of the children's parents on their wedding day and later, with little Connie around the age of two. Twila glanced across the room where Connie was standing and noticed she was looking at the pictures too. Twila wondered what was going through her younger sister's mind.

The last song was finished, the goodbyes said, and the group filed out of the house. They walked over to the school to enjoy the hot chocolate and refreshments some of the church ladies had set out for them.

Though they were tired from a late night, the girls got up early the next morning. There was plenty to do before their Christmas visitors arrived. As they sat down to a breakfast of scrambled eggs, the girls chattered to Mother about the events of the evening before. Apparently the songs were still running through Robbie's mind because he started singing, "Glo-oo-ooo-oo-ri-a, in exshell-sees day-o!"

Dad placed a piece of toast on his plate and shushed him, telling him to eat. Robbie obediently ate several bites and then broke out into song again. Dad chuckled. "Can't get that song out of your mind, can you? Well, you finish your breakfast first, and then you can sing all you want."

Grandpa and Grandma Yutzy arrived that morning, and by afternoon, Uncle James's family pulled into the lane. There was a happy hubbub of greetings as rooms were shown to the visitors and suitcases brought in. Amid the laughter and chatter of the children, Twila heard Aunt Danette say, "Now we want to fit into the way you do things. I know you keep a pretty strict schedule with Tanisha and all. Please let us know if we do anything wrong in relating to Tanisha. James and I want to do all we can to support you."

"Thank you," Mother replied warmly. "We really appreciate that. We don't want to let Tanisha's behavior control our visit or make things so rigid we can't enjoy our time together. But we *are* hoping to keep our family routine as much the same as possible. We set up a play area in the basement for the children and some easy chairs down there for the adults. If the weather's nice, the children can always play outside. We don't want the extra excitement to be too much for Tanisha."

Twila wandered into the living room where Marilyn was visiting with Grandma Yutzy. Grandma quickly included Twila in the conversation, wanting to know about her interests and what she'd been doing. Grandpa sat in the recliner, a cup of coffee in hand. Neither Dad nor Mother drank coffee, but when Grandpa Yutzy came, Mother pulled out the seldom-used coffee maker, and for the length of their stay the smell of freshly brewed coffee often lingered in the air.

Grandpa sipped his coffee and occasionally added to the conversation or chuckled when the girls shared an amusing story.

Dad and Uncle James came in, and soon they and Grandpa were discussing a building project Grandpa was working on. Later Mother and Aunt Danette joined them in the living room. Mother motioned to Tanisha, who was looking at a book, and pulled her onto her lap. Tanisha was calm and quiet. So far she seemed to be handling the commotion quite well.

Uncle James's had five lively boys, so when the noise level got too high, the men drifted to chairs in the basement where they could keep a closer eye on the children. Grandpa challenged cousin Kenneth to a game of ping-pong. After he was finished, others of the grandchildren wanted to take their turn playing Grandpa, though they knew there was little likelihood of winning.

When they were tired of playing, Grandpa sank into an easy chair and the children gathered around him. Grandpa asked them, "Did you know that it takes only twelve days for a baby to have a million heartbeats?"

"Wow, that's a lot!" exclaimed Kenneth.

"It is a lot," agreed Grandpa. "It takes thirty-one years to have one billion heartbeats and thirty-one thousand years to have one trillion heartbeats."

When the children finished marveling over the numbers, Grandpa went on, "Isn't it amazing how the Lord has made our bodies? It reminds me of the verses in Psalms where it says we are fearfully and wonderfully made."

The hours slipped by, with happy times of playing games, singing Christmas songs, and reading the story of Jesus' birth, or just family talk. When the children got restless and ran out of things to do, Grandpa kept them entertained with interesting stories and unique facts or quizzed them with mental math problems.

Though Uncle James and his family tried hard to honor Dad and Mother's wishes about relating to Tanisha, they apparently still didn't understand a few things. Keith was near Tanisha's age, and Aunt Danette encouraged him to be kind to Tanisha, sitting beside her and doing quiet things like looking at books. Though outwardly all looked fine, Twila knew Tanisha's tendency to take advantage of the attention from someone outside her own family. Mother was trying to keep a careful eye on Tanisha, but with everything going on, she didn't notice when Keith was engaging with Tanisha. Twila wanted to alert Mother, but somehow she never had a good opportunity.

One day after dinner, Dad came into the living room and found Keith sitting on the floor beside Tanisha, helping her put a puzzle together. His eyebrows rose, and he promptly sent Tanisha out to Mother in the kitchen. Then he called the rest of the boys to the living room for a talk.

Dad looked around the circle of boys in front of him. "I want to explain some things to you about Tanisha. When she was living in her other home, some very sad things happened to her. She didn't have enough to eat or a mother and a father to take care of her like you have. She had to take care of herself. When Tanisha came to our house, she didn't trust us. She didn't want to obey, and she didn't know how to love. She was very angry and scared. Because of this, she has had a lot of trouble learning to play appropriately with other children without our help. We need to restrict her time with other people outside our own family until she learns acceptable behavior with us. Now that she has a family to love and care for her, she's slowly learning to love and trust us. I know Tanisha looks like someone fun to play with, but she still needs some time yet before she's ready to play with other children."

Dad reached out and tousled Keith's hair. "Do you understand what I'm saying? Do you think you can remember that Tanisha isn't ready to play with you until she learns to trust her own family better?"

Kenneth replied for all the boys, "Sure, we can do what you say! Mom and Dad told us some of this stuff already."

"They told us we must follow your rules," said Kyle. "But may we talk to her and say hi?"

"Sure!" said Dad. "You may smile at her and say good morning or excuse me or hello, but that's all." After some more discussion, the boys ran off to pull on warm clothes. Suzanne, Connie, and Rita also dressed for the cold and went outside with them.

Robbie pleaded to go too, but Mother reminded him it was nap-time. She led him to the living room to read his naptime stories, but he was restless and whiney and didn't want to sit on Mother's lap. Grandma had spent a lot of time reading to him earlier, and now he protested that he wanted Grandma to read to him.

Mother turned the small boy around on her lap so she could look him directly in the eye. "Grandma is resting, so she cannot read to you. And besides, you are Mother's little boy. You like having Grandma read to you, don't you? It's okay to love Grandma and Aunt Danette, but you can love Mother best."

After that Robbie seemed to relax. Mother read to him and then rocked him for a long time. At a motion from Mother, Twila handed her the couch throw, and Mother tucked it close around him.

Robbie's eyes drooped, and it wasn't long until he had drifted off. When she was sure he was asleep, Mother spoke softly to Marilyn and Twila. "Why don't you sort some clothes and wash a load of dresses? I'm afraid we're going to run out soon."

Marilyn and Twila worked together to get a load of laundry ready for the washer. Marilyn was filling the soap dispenser on the washing machine when Aunt Danette entered the room with two dresses draped over her arm. "I heard your mother ask you to run a load of wash through. I was wondering if you would have room yet for two more dresses."

"Sure," Marilyn replied. "I think we can easily fit those two in yet."

Aunt Danette handed her the dresses and thanked her. Then before leaving the room, she said sternly, "And don't you try to figure out how many yards of fabric goes into those dresses either!" With twinkling eyes she turned and sailed out of the laundry room.

The two girls giggled. Aunt Danette definitely had her own brand of humor, and life was never dull when she was around.

"She's a tall woman and built bigger than some people, but I sure wouldn't call Aunt Danette fat," said Twila, between spells of stifled laughter.

After three activity-filled days, Grandpa's and Uncle James's visit came to an end. They left in the morning right after breakfast, and suddenly the house seemed much too quiet and empty. But the stillness didn't last for long. In spite of everyone's best efforts, three days seemed to be the limit of Tanisha's endurance. The first time Mother gave Tanisha a command, she fell completely apart and threw herself down on the floor. She rolled and kicked, screaming and crying at the top of her lungs.

Connie was weepy and irritable. Suzanne couldn't resist teasing her, and they promptly started arguing.

Marilyn glanced around the cluttered house and sighed. "Our visitors barely step out the door and everyone's fighting. What kind of family are we anyway?"

Robbie pulled on her hand. "I'm not fighting," he remarked solemnly.

"No, you're not," agreed Marilyn. "You're being a good boy."

Rita twirled the end of her braid around her finger and said crossly, "I wasn't fighting either, and you don't need to make it sound like I was!"

Before anyone could say more, Mother entered the room. "Why don't we all pitch in and clean up the worst of the clutter? I'll heat up some leftovers for lunch, and then this afternoon you girls are free to read a book, take a nap, or whatever you like. But it must be something quiet!"

The other girls started working. Mother bent down and tried to gather Tanisha up in her arms. But she resisted so fiercely to being held that Mother let her lie there. When she had worn herself out, Mother picked her up and carried her to the rocking chair. She wrapped a blanket snugly around the small girl, and for a long time Tanisha lay in Mother's arms, trembling and whimpering. Mother cuddled her for a long time, gently patting her and smoothing back loose curls of hair.

The rest of Christmas vacation wasn't the relaxing time Twila had looked forward to. It seemed nothing went right, and she was relieved when the morning arrived that they could go back to school.

But even that morning was miserable. Connie cried over everything and couldn't seem to pull herself together enough to get ready. She was sure she was going to have a test in English. She hadn't studied and knew she would fail it.

Suzanne looked at her incredulously. "You know we never have a test the first day back to school! The teacher never gives us one until later."

But Connie sobbed drearily that she was sure she remembered the teacher saying there would be a test.

"Listen, Connie," said Mother gently. "I'll write a note and let your teacher know you're not ready for a test. Now I want you to go and put on your school clothes. When that's done, I'll tell you what to do next. Everything will be okay," Mother soothed.

When Connie had gone to her bedroom, Suzanne looked at Mother in amazement. "What's wrong with her, and why does she think she'll have a test today, of all things? She's not even making sense."

"She's just a little confused right now," Mother said gently. "Christmas and birthdays are sometimes difficult for adopted children. Maybe Connie's been thinking about her birth family, and it's making her feel mixed up and sad. I'll try to have a talk with her later."

"I saw her looking at that picture of her birth parents at Grandma Weatherby's," Twila remarked. "Maybe that got her thinking."

Mother shook her head. "I don't know. You could be right."

"But Mother," protested Suzanne, "we're her family now! Why would she be sad, thinking about her birth family? Aren't we good enough?"

Mother flipped another pancake. "It's not that we're not good enough. It's just that her birth family fills a special spot in her heart that we can never fill. We are Connie's second family, and we'll never be able to take the place of her first family. And we don't want to. Her birth family is part of her life story. If we willingly accept that, it will be easier for Connie to accept us and the fact that she has two families."

Suzanne plopped a bag of finger Jell-O into her lunch box. "I still don't understand why Connie would care so much about a family that wasn't even that nice to her."

Mother poured some maple syrup from a jug into a small pitcher. "Think about it, Suzanne. What if something happened today to all of us and you had no family left, and you went to live with a new family you didn't even know. No matter how kind they were to you, you would still always have a special spot in your heart for us, wouldn't you?"

Understanding dawned on Suzanne's face. "Of course! You're my family!"

"Exactly," said Mother. "That's the way Connie feels. Her birth family with it all its imperfections is still her family. Another thing to remember is that all children are different. One child may not feel such a strong loyalty to her birth family as the next child. Personality, environment, and personal memories all influence how a child views his birth family."

Twila carried a pitcher of orange juice to the table. "We just take so much for granted with our families. Makes me feel almost guilty that I have it so nice when other children have such hard things to work through."

Mother nodded. "We do have much to be thankful for, growing up in Christian homes. In the meantime, try to be patient with Connie. Also, I'd rather you girls didn't discuss her among yourselves. If any of us were Connie, I don't think we'd like to find out that others were talking about us."

Connie came out to the kitchen dressed for school, but the tears still trickled down her cheeks. When Mother told her to put on her shoes, she sat down in the middle of the floor to slip them on. Robbie, seeing his older sister's distress, went over and silently began rubbing her shoulders. Every so often he bent down to look into her face and then wordlessly went back to his ministrations of comfort.

Mother patiently walked Connie through each step of getting ready for school, and by the time she walked out the door, she was in a much better frame of mind.

If Mother did talk to Connie about what was bothering her, Twila wasn't around to hear it. She did, however, observe that Connie gradually returned to her happy self.

And so the days of winter trickled by—some peaceful days, and some not so nice. But on the whole, Twila was grateful to notice a new tranquility coming to their family, more than there had been for a long time.

CHAPTER FIFTEEN

Hugs for Mother

February slipped by unseasonably warm, with everyone predicting an early spring. But, as if to prove how unpredictable the weather can be in the north, the temperatures dropped suddenly, turning bitterly cold. Dad announced one morning that it was twenty below zero.

Twila stepped out the back door with a bag of trash in each hand. She gave the door a kick with her foot to close it, and it creaked shut behind her. As she walked to the burn barrel, the snow popped and crunched under her feet. Each breath was burningly cold as she drew it into her lungs.

Twila lifted the grate off the top of the burn barrel and dumped the bags of trash inside. She pulled the box of matches out of her pocket and tried to light a match. Finding it too clumsy with her gloves on, she pulled them off. Within moments she had a fire going, but by then her fingers were numb. She replaced the grate and stood for a few minutes, watching to see that the fire didn't go out. Shivering with cold, she stamped back into the house.

As she took off her boots and hung up her coat, Marilyn called from the kitchen, "Do you know where Suzanne is?"

Twila stepped into the kitchen, rubbing her hands together, and responded, "No, I don't. I haven't seen her for a while."

Rita entered the kitchen with Robbie in tow and said, "I think she's still out doing the chicken chores."

Twila was surprised. "Robbie, why aren't you out there with her? Did Mother tell you it was too cold to be outside?" Robbie loved the chickens and usually never missed an opportunity to go with the girls.

Rita giggled. "He won't go out anymore ever since that black rooster flogged him. He's scared."

Robbie nodded solemnly in agreement. "Yes, I'm scared! I'm scared it will peck me!"

Twila picked up the little boy and twirled him around the kitchen. "I don't blame you. I don't like that rooster either." Robbie laughed as she put him down and then ran off to play farming with Rita.

"Mother said you're supposed to peel these potatoes for supper," Marilyn informed Twila. "She said Suzanne can make some bars if she wants to, but if she doesn't get in from doing chores, she won't have time before supper."

Twila pulled out a knife and a peeler and stepped over to the sink to start her task. She looked at the mound of potatoes in the bowl and said unhappily, "Why so many?"

Marilyn shrugged. "Jeff's going to eat supper with us tonight, so I suppose there's a few extra." She sliced a hardboiled egg and dumped it into the macaroni salad she was making.

Mother came through the kitchen with an armload of towels, and right behind her followed Tanisha with her own arms full. Her face glimmered with a look of faint happiness. Slowly she was finding the joy of obeying sweetly, and more and more she was taking pleasure in her accomplishments. The back door banged shut and soon Suzanne entered, bringing with her the air of activity that seemed to always follow her around.

"I asked Mother if I could make some bars, and she said I could," Suzanne announced as she pulled a cookbook down from the shelf. "I'm going to make lemon bars. Those are my favorite."

"Well, you'd better hurry if you want to serve them for supper or they won't be cool enough to eat," Marilyn said a trifle irritably. Having Suzanne in the kitchen was a trial of patience. She seemed to fill the whole kitchen as she rummaged in the cupboards for measuring cups and ingredients.

Mother entered the kitchen to supervise the supper preparations, and she and the girls laughed and talked as they worked. "Mother," Suzanne called from where she had her head poked into the fridge. "Where's the lemon juice?"

Mother went to help her look. "Isn't it right there in the door? That's usually where we keep it."

Suzanne shook her head. "There's none here." Mother checked over her shoulder and then checked in the cupboard for any new bottles. When no lemon juice was to be found, Suzanne wailed, "But how can I make lemon bars without lemon juice?"

Mother glanced at the clock. "Marilyn and Twila, I guess you girls will have to run in to the grocery store in Kenton and buy some. Next time, Suzanne, make sure we have all the ingredients before you start baking." Mother got her purse and handed some money to Marilyn. "Drive carefully. It's cold out there, and the roads are slippery," she cautioned.

The girls were soon on their way. They were just coming into town when, without warning, the vehicle in front of them slowed down to turn onto a side road. They were just crossing an icy spot in the road, and Marilyn knew there was no way she could slow down in time. Not wanting to rear-end the vehicle, she whipped the wheel to turn into the driveway of the town's only gas station. She was going too fast to make the turn properly, causing her to plow into a towering bank of snow.

"Marilyn!" gasped Twila.

Marilyn's hands were trembling, and she said rather shakily, "Well, at least I didn't hit that vehicle."

She put the van in reverse, but the tires just spun. "I guess we'll have to go into the store and call Mother. Maybe Dad will be home by now and can come pull me out." As the girls jumped out of the van, they were vastly relieved to see Bob Graham just coming out of the gas station.

Seeing their predicament, he came to investigate. "Girl, you'd better slow down next time before you decide to turn!" he exclaimed.

"But I wasn't planning to turn," Marilyn sputtered. "A vehicle slowed down in front of me, and I was on an ice patch. I couldn't stop in time. I thought it was better to hit the snowbank than to hit the other car."

Mr. Graham chuckled and went to get a tow strap from the back of his truck. Giving Marilyn instructions on what to do, he pulled her out. With grateful thanks and a sigh of relief, the girls were on their way.

By the time they got home, Dad and Jeff were already there. While the girls helped Mother finish getting supper ready, they described their mishap. Mother said gratefully, "I'm just glad no one was hurt."

Dad chuckled, and Jeff grinned. "That's girl driving for you!" Jeff teased.

As often happened, the family lingered around the table enjoying the chance to catch up on the happenings of the day or discuss life in general.

"You know what?" Suzanne asked Jeff. "Ricky told Rita that Janice has leprosy, and she actually believed him." Condescension dripped from her voice.

Rita flushed and squirmed in her chair. Jeff grinned, but seeing her embarrassment, refrained from laughing. "Well, shall I tell you something that shows how dumb I was when I was little?"

At Rita's eager nod, Jeff went on. "Before we added on to our church, it was very small and crowded. On Sundays when we had Sunday school or on Wednesday evenings when we gathered for prayer, we would pull curtains to divide the auditorium into classrooms. On prayer meeting evenings, one of the youth boys would always faithfully pray for those behind the Iron Curtain. I thought he was praying for the women and girls because they were on the other side of the curtain. It was years before I realized he was actually praying for the persecuted Christians in Communist countries. So," Jeff said, grinning, "you're not the only one who gets mixed up about things."

Rita giggled. "Even I know about Communism and the Iron Curtain. Mother read a book to us about it one time."

They visited awhile longer; then the phone rang and someone wanted to talk to Dad. Mother glanced around the table and said briskly, "Well, girls, these dishes aren't going to get done by themselves so I think you'd better get at it. Connie, you need to hustle off to bed. You had a hard time getting up this morning. Apparently you need more sleep."

Connie's face crumpled. "Why do I have to go to bed before anyone else? I always get the worst punishments."

Mother was about to speak when Jeff said, "Hey, I wouldn't complain if I was you! Your Mom might decide to do what my Dad did to me one time."

Connie stopped pouting and asked, "What was that?"

"I kept complaining that my brothers and sisters never got punished as badly as I did. One day Dad told me that since I thought the others had it so much nicer than I did, he would give me a week to find out if it was true. Whatever consequences the others got, I would get it too, whether I had done anything wrong or not. Well, the *worst* thing that could possibly happen, happened! One of my older sisters wasn't washing the dishes clean, so Mom told her she had to wash dishes after every meal for three days. So when her three days were up, *I* had to wash dishes for three days."

Connie's dark eyes were sparkling. "So did you make sure you never complained again?"

Jeff blushed. "I was pretty bullheaded back then," he admitted, "so I'm sure I complained plenty of times after that. But at least for a while, I was much more careful."

Robbie, who had earlier wandered off to his toys, came up to Jeff with his tractor and wagon. "It's broke, Jeff. Can you fix it?"

Connie went off to bed, Suzanne pulled out some homework, and Rita and Marilyn went out to clean up the supper dishes. While Twila cleared off the table, she watched as Jeff got down on the floor with Robbie. Robbie scooted close beside Jeff, and the two dark heads bent over the broken toy. It was ironic that Robbie, with his straight black hair, looked almost more Hammond than she and her sisters did. But when he lifted his head to ask Jeff a question, the most definite similarities stopped.

"Can you fix it, Jeff?" the small boy wondered.

"Yeah, I think so. Run get me a pliers. I think I'll be able to bend the metal down so you can use it."

Dad had finished his phone call and was coming back into the room when he heard Jeff's request. "Did you say you needed a pliers?" He reached into his pocket to pull out a pair. Dad almost always carried pliers in his side pocket.

Jeff handed Dad the toy and explained what he thought could be done to fix it. In no time, Dad expertly mended the broken toy, and a happy little boy began pushing his tractor and wagon around again.

Jeff stood up and stretched. "Well, I should get going if I want to get home to Mom and Dad's before midnight." Jeff reached down and tousled Robbie's hair as he drove past with his tractor.

"I should take you home with me for the weekend. You could keep me awake while I drive."

"No!" said Robbie emphatically. "I'm staying home with Mama!" Jeff laughed. He thanked Mother for the supper, told the girls goodbye, and went out the door.

"Don't fall asleep while you're driving!" Rita called anxiously after him.

"I won't," came drifting back into the kitchen.

The next day was Saturday, and Twila had just finished cleaning and vacuuming the living room when Rita and Robbie came in, all set to play house.

"I played farming with you yesterday, so you need to play house with me today," Rita informed Robbie. Robbie amiably agreed. He was happy to have a day with Rita at home to play with, and it didn't matter much to him what they played. But Twila was not impressed. When Rita and Robbie set up housekeeping, they usually made one grand mess.

"I just cleaned, and now they want to mess it all up," she complained to Mother.

"Let them play," Mother replied, but she turned to the other two. "But remember—if you make a mess, you clean it up."

"We will!" Rita promised.

"We will," Robbie echoed.

They set up house in a corner of the living room, and a little later Rita announced to Robbie, "I'm going to the store. You watch baby Annie for me." Rita left for another part of the living room, and Robbie picked up the dolly and cried, "Wa-a-a! I want my mommy."

Rita turned around and said, "No, she doesn't. She's sleeping. She doesn't even know I'm gone. Put her back in bed."

Robbie laid the doll back down in its bed and puttered around the little house while Rita continued on her shopping trip.

When Robbie wasn't paying attention, Twila asked Mother, "Did you hear what Robbie said? How does he know so much about how a baby feels without its mother when he's so little? One time I showed him a picture of a starving child from another country and he told me, 'The baby say, "I want hold." ' How does he know all that?"

Mother paused from where she was washing small finger-prints from the dining room windows. "I don't suppose he really does know. It's more of a subconscious thing stemming from his own experiences. Dad and I are hoping that we can teach him—and really, all of you children—to take the unfortunate circumstances of life and use them to help you to be more compassionate. Robbie has a lot of life's experiences ahead to test him, but I'm glad to see that he's already demonstrating compassion with just a dolly."

Marilyn, who had been listening in the doorway, crossed to the table and sat down. She sighed with uncharacteristic pessimism. "Is it possible for our family to do anything right? Just the other day one of the girls at school said her mom thinks if we would just love Tanisha more, we wouldn't have all these problems."

Mother smiled wryly. "As for doing anything right, it's only with God's help that we can. What do you think about loving Tanisha more? How would *you* answer that question?"

Marilyn sat for a long time, drumming her fingers on the table in much the same way Dad did when he was pondering something. Twila twisted her dusting rag into a tight rope as she struggled to find an answer in her own mind.

Finally Marilyn spoke. "I feel guilty sometimes because I don't *feel* like loving Tanisha, and I wonder—if I had a better attitude, would she do better? I mean, would *I* feel like being nice to others if people felt about me the way I sometimes feel about her?"

Mother bent down and swiped at a smudge she had missed. She straightened and looked first at Marilyn and then Twila. "There's an element of truth in what you say, Marilyn. Love is very important. It's a well-known fact that babies will die in orphanages for lack of touch and love. Elderly people will give up and die if they have no one to love and care for them.

"But I think there's something we foster and adoptive families overlook sometimes. We have rose-tinted ideas of how we'll bring needy children into our homes and just love them back to emotional health. People looking on expect the same. We forget that, though human love is essential, it will never be enough for any child. Only God can reach down and heal the wounded places in a child's heart.

"Yes, God uses families in wonderful ways to help restore an emotionally damaged child, but only He can cleanse and heal. There are some hurts that cannot be kissed away. No amount of hugs and loving parenting can erase all the effects of trauma and neglect. If we think it's up to us as a family to do all the healing, we set ourselves up for failure. We are in partnership with God, fighting for the hearts and souls of each child. But we must never think the success and healing of a child solely depends on us."

A look of relief crossed Marilyn's face. "I guess that's what Dad was trying to tell us in devotions that time when he read Luke 4:18, about Jesus coming to heal the brokenhearted. I know I need to do my part and keep on loving Tanisha even when I don't feel like it. But it's nice to know that all the responsibility doesn't rest on us."

Twila loosened her rag. It hung limp in her hand, the creases still showing. She spoke slowly. "Maybe it's my imagination, but it doesn't seem like Tanisha's so hard to love anymore. I'm not sure if *she* changed or if *I* did."

"I suppose we've all changed," said Mother. "But I really think Tanisha has improved the last while—more than we realize. Did you notice she's much more willing to obey commands? She's not so resistant, and she's quicker to obey."

Marilyn grinned, once more her philosophical self. "Well, we'll enjoy it while it lasts!"

"Might as well," Twila agreed. "Her behavior can change faster than any child I know!"

Robbie ran up to Mother with a doll, its blanket trailing on the floor. "Mama! Mama! Wrap up this doll for me," he ordered.

"Robbie! Say *please*," instructed Mother.

"Please!" said Robbie, his tone still demanding.

"No, Robbie," said Mother. "Say *please* patiently."

Robbie straightened up and took a deep breath. "Please patiently," he said with the proper respect in his voice.

"There, that's much better!" Mother chuckled as she reached for the doll and wrapped it snugly in its blanket. Glancing out the window, she said, "Oh, Dad's home from the Webers', and it looks like he's got that wood splitter he was hoping to borrow."

With the sudden drop in temperatures, the wood supply was being used up more rapidly than Dad had anticipated. He had decided to split some more wood to last the rest of the winter.

"Robbie," said Mother. "Why don't you get your coat and boots and go out with Dad for a while? Tanisha, you can go too. It's not nearly as cold as it was yesterday. It would do you both good to get a few minutes of fresh air."

Mother had just finished helping Robbie and Tanisha with their mittens and was ushering them out the door when Suzanne and Connie came stamping into the house. They had gone with Dad to the Webers' and were brimming with news.

"Mother!" exclaimed Suzanne before she had even taken off her coat. "Do you remember that other Weber family that was at the adoption picnic? They had a really cute little boy named Dominic. When we were with Dad just now at Dennis Weber's, they told us that the other Weber family gave their little boy away. They didn't want him anymore! Mother, how could they *do* such a thing! Did you know about it?"

Rita looked wistfully at Mother. "You mean you can do that? If an adoption doesn't work out, you can give the child away?" Twila wondered if Rita was thinking of Tanisha and hoping that Mother and Dad would decide to do the same with her if things got too difficult.

Mother looked around at her five daughters waiting for an answer. She sighed. "Yes, I had heard about it. It's called disrupting an adoption."

Before Mother could say any more, Suzanne interrupted. "Isn't it just awful?"

Mother looked thoughtfully at Suzanne and then at each of the other girls. "It *is* very sad," she agreed. "But we must be very, very careful how we judge this situation. We know ourselves how difficult it can be to have a child with attachment problems in the home. There could be many reasons why the Webers felt that disrupting the adoption was the only option left. Maybe they didn't have the house space to keep him and the other children safe. You know how important it is for a child with RAD to have a bedroom of his own. Maybe the family couldn't afford that, and maybe they couldn't find or afford therapy and respite care if Dominic needed those things. Or maybe they didn't have the support and understanding of their church and extended families. Maybe it was simply that they were wearing out. Sometimes parents don't have the strength and energy to parent a very needy child for the long journey to healing. There could be a lot of reasons why it just didn't work to keep Dominic in their home. It must be a very painful time for them, and we certainly don't want to add to their hurt by being critical."

"It's very sad!" agreed Twila. "Half of me wonders how they could let him go, but the other half understands. Back before we had the alarm and before Tanisha started therapy, I wouldn't have cared one bit if you and Dad would have asked Mrs. Gunther to place Tanisha somewhere else."

Marilyn finally spoke. "You know, if Tanisha had to leave now, I really think I would miss her a lot. But I can see how hard it would be to have a child with RAD if we didn't have the love and understanding of our family and church. I know I've been irked several times when people think we don't love Tanisha enough, but really, most of the church people have been very good to us. Remember how Elva made hot lunch for us when we forgot? And Brenda Ramer took us to school for the first half of the year, and she still takes us quite often."

"And we've gotten thinking-of-you cards, and someone even gave us flowers!" added Connie.

Suzanne grinned. "Don't forget the meals some of the church ladies brought. I remember we got some really good desserts."

"Yes, people *have* been very good to us!" Mother agreed. "I've appreciated so much the things they've done for us, but I think their prayer support means the most to me. Sometimes when I'm discouraged, it gives me a lift just to have someone say they're praying for our family."

"People were really good to us over the time our baby Michael died too," said Suzanne. "We're going to have to make sure we treat others as well as they've treated us."

"You're right," agreed Mother. "Even if we'll never be able to repay all that others have done for us, we still need to do what we can. This is one of the blessings of church life. When the going gets rough, we can be there for each other."

Tanisha and Robbie came into the house, and that was the end of the mother and daughter conversation.

"We're cold!" Robbie announced.

Tanisha kicked off her boots. She went promptly over to the house that Robbie and Rita had been playing with earlier and dumped out a basket of doll clothes. Then she gave one of the dolls a kick.

"Hmmm," said Mother. "I wonder what's up with that? I think you missed Mother while you were outside, and now you're cold and you want me to rock you." Mother swooped up the little girl and grabbed an afghan from the couch. She sat down in the rocker and wrapped Tanisha in the blanket. "Now, tell me what you did out there."

Tanisha snuggled against Mother but didn't answer right away. Then she said softly, "We were helpin' Dad."

Robbie was jumping up and down. "Dad started the split wooder, and it made a roaring sound. And I covered my ears." He clapped his hands over his ears to demonstrate.

Mother smiled at the small boy's excitement and then looked down at Tanisha. "How did you help Dad?" she wondered.

Robbie was jumping again. "Um, um, we—"

But Mother held up her hand. "Let Tanisha tell us this time."

Tanisha still struggled to converse nicely with Mother or any of the family, but at last she said, "We gave Dad chunks of wood. But most of them were too heavy for us."

"And then Dad put them in the splitter and zoom! It came apart!" Robbie gestured dramatically, his eyes shining.

The phone rang and Twila jumped up to answer it. Aunt Julia's voice, hasty and urgent, came over the line. "Ask your mother if it's okay to bring Ricky and Justin over. Janice fell and cut a nasty gash so close to her eye that we weren't able to fix it ourselves. We're taking her to the emergency room."

Twila quickly relayed the message and at Mother's nod, she said, "Sure, bring them over!"

Not much later, Uncle Jerry's pulled in, and Ricky and Justin got out of the van. They came into the house, and Marilyn helped Justin out of his coat and boots. The instant Ricky had shrugged out of his, he and the middle girls dashed off to the basement to play ping-pong.

At first, Justin looked a little uncertain to be deserted by his last family member, but he went willingly enough when Marilyn led him to the toy corner in the living room. He looked solemnly at the tractor that Robbie generously offered him, but refused to take it. Suddenly he picked up a box of Legos and tipped it upside down. He laughed delightedly as the pieces clattered noisily to the floor. Robbie giggled, and the older girls couldn't help but laugh at the pleased expression on Justin's face.

Tanisha sat up on Mother's lap and said solemnly, "Hmmm. I wonder what's up with that?"

Mother and the girls exchanged amused glances over Tanisha's head. It was so wonderful and sometimes humorous to hear what was going on in Tanisha's mind!

As usual, there was an increase in noise and activity with Ricky around, but everything went well. A couple of hours later, Uncle Jerry and Aunt Julia came to collect the boys. They brought Janice and little Kendra into the house with them. The girls gathered around to listen to the report of their doctor visit and inspect the neat row of stitches that traveled from Janice's eyelid, through her eyebrow, and up onto her forehead.

Janice enjoyed all the attention and proudly showed the girls a big round sticker she had received from the nurse for her bravery.

At Mother's invitation, Uncle Jerry's whole family stayed for a pizza supper. There was a happy hubbub as they gathered around the table to eat.

Twila liked being with Uncle Jerry's family. They were comfortable people to be around. Perhaps it was because Uncle Jerry and Aunt Julia had calmly accepted Tanisha just as she was. They had also accepted the changes in lifestyle that had come with Tanisha joining their family. Maybe it was also because Twila's family had loved and accepted hyperactive little Ricky when he had come to live with Uncle Jerry as a six-year-old.

Throughout the meal, Twila observed the changes that his growing family had brought to Uncle Jerry's life. He cut Justin's pizza for him, encouraged Janice to eat, and quieted Ricky with a look when he got to talking too loudly at the other end of the table. Later he held little Kendra so Aunt Julia could eat in peace without little fingers reaching for everything. All this was calmly done in the midst of visiting with Mother and Dad. Uncle Jerry and Aunt Julia had both been older when they had made the abrupt change from single life to marriage and parenthood. It had not been without its adjustments, but they had done it gracefully.

Soon after supper, Uncle Jerrys gathered their little people and left. Later when dishes were done, the house was tidy, and the evening baths were taken, the family gathered in the living room for a Bible story and prayer. It was Robbie's turn to pray, and his prayers usually consisted of a long list of thanksgivings. He thanked God for each member of the family several times and mentioned any other extended family and anyone from church who came to his mind.

Twila held her breath and listened intently. Robbie's prayers were always so original that you never knew what to expect. He thanked God that Uncle Jerrys had come for supper and thanked God that the doctors had fixed up Janice's eye. He paused a moment and added, "And please be with Janice's grandchildren!"

Twila nearly choked as she tried to hold back the laughter. Marilyn coughed suspiciously, and one of the younger girls snickered out loud before she caught herself. Blissfully innocent, Robbie finished his prayer, and then Dad prayed. When they got up from praying a few minutes later, amusement still glimmered in the family's eyes.

Over the next few weeks, Tanisha continued to make steady improvement. The other girls were excited, but though Twila was happy for the changes, she refused to get her hopes up too high. Too many times in the past, Tanisha had done better, but then before long, her good behavior had seemed to blow away with the wind. But as time went on and Tanisha's negative habits continued to diminish, Twila's hopes began to rise. It was delightful to see a sweet, happy little girl emerge from the sullen, angry one. It was wonderful to see who Tanisha really was, instead of the phony pretend person she had so often portrayed.

Mother began to let Tanisha play more with Robbie, and she spent a lot of time teaching her how to share and play nicely. Though Tanisha was learning, she still tended to be greedy and grab toys from Robbie whether she actually wanted them or not. Once when she was being especially selfish, Robbie told her bluntly, "I don't like you!"

In a patronizing tone, Tanisha flashed back, "Well, that's too bad, because I don't like you either!"

Mealtimes that had once been such a problem for Tanisha, because Dad and Mother wouldn't let her eat all she wanted, were becoming less so. Mother worked hard to teach her that the food would not run out, and the girls still often sang Marilyn's song, "There will always be food on the table."

In the midst of all these improvements, the girls wondered why Mother and Dad still clung to the tightly structured schedule. "Tanisha is doing so well! Can't you be a little easier on her?" they wondered.

Mother explained, "When someone is desperately ill and in the hospital and then begins to get better, the doctors don't take them off IVs and medication too quickly. There's too much risk of a setback. It works the same with children who are emotionally damaged. We don't want to be too quick to take away from Tanisha the very things that are helping her get better. And remember, even though she's much better, it will be a long time before she's healthy and strong enough to be away from me for any length of time, or be without a good amount of structure."

Suzanne stirred impatiently. "I just wish this whole project wouldn't have to take so long!"

The conversation ended when Tanisha came into the kitchen. She turned her face up to Mother and said, "I'm done folding those washcloths, Mother. What do you want me to do now?"

Mother checked to be sure the job had been done correctly. Then she said, "You did a good job. Now I want you to give me a big hug!" She scooped the little girl into her arms. Tanisha wrapped her arms around Mother's neck and squeezed tightly. "I love you, Mother! Promise!"

When Dad came home that evening, Tanisha went dancing to the door to welcome him home. But when she reached out to hug him, he said, "Wait a minute! Did you hug Mother today?"

Tanisha's eyes were shining. "Oh, yes, I gave her lots of hugs today!"

Dad looked at Mother for confirmation. Mother nodded and smiled. "She's right. She did very well today!"

A light came on in Dad's eyes as he picked up his little girl and held her close.

CHAPTER SIXTEEN

My Heart Says
I Love You

Twila slowly strolled through the woods on her way back from the Grahams, enjoying the lush, leafy green. Spring had come with first the wild leeks and then the spring beauties. Later had come the trilliums and ferns. The trees had leafed out and the flowering crab tree, which the Hammonds had planted in memory of Michael, had bloomed more beautifully than ever.

School was out, and the garden was planted and thriving. Mother had even planted some extra this year for selling—a sign that Tanisha was improving and that the Hammonds were learning to adjust to life with a needy child in the family.

It was now early summer, and strawberries were in season. That is why Twila had gone to the Grahams. Mother had sent her over with a small jar of fresh strawberry jam. She had stayed to visit with Mrs. Graham for a little while.

Twila's walk brought her out of the woods and into the backyard. She looked around contentedly, taking in the green grass and blooming flowers. Her roving eyes caught sight of Suzanne and Connie sneaking up to the playhouse. Twila hastened her steps to see what mischief the girls were up to now. She came within view of the playhouse just in time to see Suzanne and Connie standing at the door. They tipped their heads back and began singing "Joy to the World" at the top of their lungs.

The door burst open and out popped two irate little housewives. "Go away!" shouted Rita. "We don't want you to sing Christmas carols for us."

Tanisha looked up at Rita and promptly echoed, "Go away!"

The two older girls ignored the shrieks and kept right on singing. In spite of the continuing protests, they sang all the way through "Joy to the World" and ended up with "We Wish You a Blessed Christmas."

"Now," said Suzanne when they had finished, "we sang for you, so you have to give us some candy."

"No! No candy," said Rita emphatically, "but you can come in and have a tea party with us. Mother gave us some milk and strawberries." Her indignation melting away, she welcomed her older sisters into the playhouse.

The four girls went inside, and soon sounds of fun and laughter floated out. Twila peeked through the window at her younger sisters crowded around the little table, enjoying their afternoon snack. She thought of joining them, but the little playhouse was already filled to capacity. She went to the house to share her amusement with Mother and Marilyn.

"Did Mrs. Graham say when she wanted me to come this week?" wondered Marilyn, when they had finished laughing over the incident.

"Oh, yes," replied Twila. "Mrs. Graham said not to bother coming this week. She and Mr. Graham are going out of state somewhere to a naturalist meeting or convention of some sort."

"My, she must be accepting her handicap better!" said Mother. "It seems she's going out and doing things more all the time instead of brooding at home."

"Oh, by the way, Twila," said Marilyn, "did I ever tell you what Mrs. Graham had to say about the picture you drew of her?"

"No, you didn't," said Twila. "I was going to ask, but I forgot all about it."

"She said your drawing wasn't too bad—better, anyway, than this modern art stuff you see nowadays. She said you made her look like a normal human even with a missing leg. But she wondered why on earth you made her nose look like a humpy dromedarian camel."

Twila giggled. "I guess that's a typical Mrs. Graham comment for you. Half compliment and half bite!"

Mother took the last batch of strawberry jam off the stove and set it on a hot pad on the kitchen table beside the row of freezer containers Marilyn had set out. She reached for a ladle and carefully poured hot jam into the containers. "Twila, why don't you get a big bowl and go cut some mint for supper? I noticed it's tall enough to cut again, and you know how Dad likes iced mint tea. Oh, and bring Tanisha in on your way back. She needs to come in and be with me for a while."

Twila grabbed a bowl and a pair of scissors and headed out the back door. She thought about the picture she had drawn of Mrs. Graham. That reminded her of the drawing of Dad that had been scribbled on and thrown into the trash can in Robbie's room. As always, when she thought of Dad's picture, she also remembered the forbidden book that had mysteriously appeared under her pillow. Somehow, those two incidents were always connected in her mind. A pang of hurt still pierced her heart when she thought of how her parents had doubted her honesty. Twila had forgiven her parents, and most of the sting had faded. But now she had a sudden flash of insight—of course Tanisha had been behind both of those incidents!

The playhouse door banged, and Tanisha came out as Twila walked past to the tea bed. "Oh, there you are, Tanisha! Mother wants you to come to the house with me as soon as I'm done cutting tea. Do you want to play some more, or do you want to help me?"

Tanisha considered for a long moment. "Did Mother say I may play a little longer?" she asked cautiously.

"That's what Mother said," Twila assured her.

Tanisha thought some more and then said, "I'll go with you."

"Well, come along then!" said Twila cheerfully.

Together they went to the tea patch. Twila cut the stalks of mint with the scissors and handed them to Tanisha to put in the bowl. The bowl was nearly full when Twila said, "Tanisha."

Tanisha looked up. "What?"

Twila fingered the leaves of the tea sprig she was holding. At last she said, "Do you remember that picture I drew of Dad? And the girls found it in the wastebasket in Robbie's room all scribbled up? And do you remember the book Mother told me not to read, and later she found it under my pillow?"

Tanisha sat still for a long time. Finally she nodded slowly. "I *think* I do."

Twila looked directly at Tanisha and kept her voice kind. "It was you that wrecked the picture. And you put the book under my pillow so I would get in trouble. Is that right?"

After a long moment, Tanisha lifted her eyes to Twila and said softly, "I know I put the book under your pillow, and I'm pretty sure I scribbled the picture too. But I can't 'member why I did all that stuff a long time ago."

Twila handed Tanisha another handful of tea leaves. "Tanisha, Mother thought I was lying about the book, and Robbie got in trouble because they thought he scribbled my picture. May I tell Mother and Dad who really did those things?"

"Am I gonna be in big trouble?" Tanisha asked in a small voice. Fear flickered in her brown eyes.

Twila gazed down at the small girl in front of her, and at last she spoke. "No, I don't think so. Mother and Dad understand how hard it was for you to learn to live with our family. I just want them to know the truth."

"Oh," said Tanisha, and then she gulped. "Okay."

As Twila searched inwardly for her own motive in bringing this up, she put her finger under Tanisha's chin so she could look straight into those troubled eyes. "Tanisha, I just want to tell you that . . . that I forgive you. And that I love you. And I really hope you can be adopted and be my little sister forever."

Tanisha sat motionless for a long moment. Twila watched as a single tear slid down her cheek and dripped off her chin. At last Tanisha looked up. "Really?"

"Of course," said Twila. She was surprised herself with how sincerely she meant it. Twila dropped her scissors in the dirt beside her and held out her arms to the little girl. Wordlessly, Tanisha wrapped her arms around Twila and hugged her fiercely. When at last she let go, Twila picked up the scissors and the bowl of tea, and the two of them walked quietly into the house together.

Mother's response when Twila told her about the scribbled picture and the book was one of relief and understanding. "Oh, Twila!" she said. "I am so sorry we didn't believe you about that book! We failed to take your word when you had never before given us reason to doubt your honesty. I'm very sorry that we were so hard on you, and I hope you can forgive Dad and me for making such a big mistake. Dad will want to apologize to you when he comes home, and we'll have to talk to Robbie too— though it wouldn't surprise me if he's totally forgotten that we blamed him for scribbling on that picture."

"It's okay, Mother," said Twila readily. "Everything was so confusing over that time. It was no wonder you and Dad didn't know what to think. I was hurt that you distrusted me, but don't worry—I haven't been holding it against you. I'm just thankful Tanisha was willing to admit the truth, and that this whole thing can be cleared up now!"

"Well, thank you," said Mother with obvious relief. "I feel like I've learned so much this past year. I just feel bad that you children had to suffer the consequences for my mistakes. It's been a difficult year for all of us, and I thank God for how well you girls have done."

A few days later the Hammonds received a call from the Leids, a family from church. They were going to Haiti for a term of service and were trying to find a place for all their animals. They had found a home for their goats and the dog, but nobody had taken the cat. It was agreed that the cat, Tilly, could come. Rita was overjoyed to have another cat about the place, but Suzanne was not impressed. "Mother, you're not going to let Rita have *another* cat in the house, are you?"

The Leids brought the cat over that same day. After they left, Marilyn tried to pick up the cat, but she jumped out of her arms. She sat down a few feet away and began to smooth her rumpled fur with her tongue. Marilyn laughed. "I don't think we have to worry about this cat wanting to come in the house. Not the way she sticks her nose in the air and acts like she's too good for people."

True to Marilyn's predictions, Tilly the cat never paid much attention to them. Rita was the only one she would allow to hold or pet her. But, sleek and black, she soon became a permanent fixture about the place. In spite of her aloofness, the Hammond family, with the exception of Suzanne, rather liked seeing her roam about the property. She was such a pretty cat.

Rita was delighted when a few days afterward, Tilly had a batch of five kittens. She came excitedly into the house to tell Mother and the other girls. "Mother, may I take Tanisha and Robbie out to see them?"

Mother looked doubtful but said, "All right, you may take them out for a peek, but don't hold the kittens. They're too little yet, and we don't want them to get hurt. Watch Robbie and Tanisha very closely," Mother cautioned.

"I'll go out with them," Marilyn offered. "I wouldn't mind seeing the kittens myself, and I'll make sure nothing happens to them."

Twila decided to go too. She followed the rest out behind the woodpile where Tilly had carefully hidden her nest. "Ooohhh!" squealed Robbie. "They're so tiny!"

"Hush," cautioned Marilyn. "Be quiet, or the mother cat might move them where we can't find them again."

"Look," said Rita. "There's one all black, one black and white, two gray kitties, and then there's this tiny white one with a few black spots on it. I like that little one the best. It's soooo cute!"

"It's so tiny. I kind of doubt it will live," said Twila.

Rita looked up anxiously. "You really think it might die?" She sighed. "Well, I guess it's not too surprising. But I sure hope she makes it."

Tanisha was enthralled with the little kitties, and once or twice a day she begged to go out to see them. On the third day, they found the tiniest kitten limp and lifeless at the edge of the nest. Rita and Connie were disappointed, but they had seen that the kitten was getting noticeably weaker. They had been expecting it, but Tanisha was devastated. She cried and cried for the poor little kitty.

"It's nice to see that she cares about animals instead of wanting to hurt them like she used to," Twila told Mother. "But it seems like she goes from one extreme to the other."

"I think that's normal," replied Mother. "I'm glad to see her showing sadness over death and pain. We'll keep trying to help her learn to have a balanced view of the death of animals and other losses that are just a part of life. Her grief right now may not be just about the kitten. She may be grieving for other losses in her life and for other painful things she's experienced. Hard as it is to watch Tanisha go through this phase, I'm glad she is. It's essential to her emotional healing that she grieve. Her tears tell me that she's getting better."

A few weeks later the peas were ready, and once again Mother and the girls picked and shelled buckets of peas. To Twila, they seemed endless.

It was interesting to note the changes in Tanisha. Last year she had wordlessly played with the pea shells Mother had given her or had just sat blankly in her chair. This year she joined in, energetically determined to keep up with the rest. She proudly dumped her small bowl of shelled peas into the big one at regular intervals.

Robbie helped for a while, but mostly ate everything he shelled. Finally, after spilling what few peas had actually managed to reach his bowl, he ran off to play. Mother allowed Tanisha to help awhile longer; then she told her it was time for her to go and play as well. "You may play on the swings or ride your bike on the sidewalk. Which do you choose?"

"But I want to help shell peas!" Tanisha protested.

"I know you do," said Mother. "But it's time to play now. When playtime is over, you may come shell peas again. There will still be plenty more peas to shell. Now choose what you want to play, or I will choose for you." Tanisha continued to whine until Mother said firmly, "Tanisha, go play on the swings."

"But I want to ride my bike," she complained.

Mother's voice was calm. "Tanisha, tell me why you didn't get to choose your play."

Tanisha sighed. "Because I whined instead of choosing right away."

"So," said Mother, "whose fault is it?"

"Mine," admitted Tanisha.

Mother smiled. "Good job!" She gave Tanisha a hug. "Now, go play on the swings."

"Why don't you just let her work if she wants to?" wondered Marilyn after she had gone. "Isn't wanting to work a good thing?"

Mother reached for the bucket and filled her pan with more peas. "Yes and no," she replied. "It's important that children learn to work and find satisfaction in it. Tanisha is learning that and is happy contributing to family life. But play is also an important part of childhood. Tanisha needs to learn to relax and be a little girl. She needs to find out that it's okay to have fun and play. But right now she's still afraid of the nice feeling that comes after having a good time. She's still overly alert to what's going on around her and that makes it hard for her to relax and enjoy playing. If we don't teach her to play, she'll grow up to be a nervous, restless adult who doesn't enjoy the pleasures of life."

"Well, she's like that already and she's not even grown-up yet," observed Suzanne.

"You're exactly right!" agreed Mother. "That's why it's so important for us to insist that she learns to play."

"It seems strange," said Twila. "The rest of us had no trouble learning to play. It's the work part that comes hard for us."

Rita walked up and plopped down in a chair. Suzanne looked at her disgustedly. "Where were *you?* It seems like you always disappear when there's work to be done. *You* sure don't need any practice at playing."

Rita reached for a bowl and said airily, "I wasn't playing! I was taking care of the cats."

Suzanne sniffed. "As if those cats need you to take care of them. The mother is doing a fine job without your help!"

Rita filled her bowl brimful of peas and began to shell. "Tilly does too need me. I take her table scraps and fill her water dish so she doesn't have to leave her babies so much."

When Suzanne opened her mouth again, Mother spoke up mildly, "Leave her alone, Suzanne. Just because you have no love for cats doesn't mean it's wrong that Rita does. And if Rita is slipping out of work, I'll take care of it. It's too big a job for you to worry about."

"When I get big," Rita announced, "I'm going to live in a cabin way back in the woods. I'm going to plant a bunch of flowers and have lots of cats."

Marilyn grinned and raised her eyebrows at Twila. She said, "Taking care of all those flowers would be fun, but being way back in the woods sounds like a rather lonely way to live."

But Rita shook her head. "I wouldn't be lonely. I'd have all my cats!"

Suzanne sniffed again but didn't make any comment.

The next day Mother and the girls went to town. Mother needed to pick up some groceries, and they made a stop at the feedstore for laying mash and cat food. On their way home, they stopped in to visit Grandma, and she insisted they stay and eat lunch with her. "It's much nicer to eat when you have someone to eat with. It's no fun having meals all by yourself."

After lunch they cleaned up the kitchen and visited awhile longer, until Tanisha became restless and Robbie was ready for a nap. When they got home, Mother instructed, "Robbie, come with me. I'm going to put you to bed. Tanisha, I want you to go and ride your bike until I call you. The rest of you girls can unload the groceries from the van."

Twila noticed Tanisha pedaling down the lane but didn't pay much attention. She took a couple of bags in each hand and carried them into the house. When she came back out, her eyes automatically scanned the driveway for Tanisha. Marilyn, who had followed her out of the house, did the same. She exclaimed, "Where's Tanisha?"

"Girls, have you seen Tanisha?" demanded Twila of her younger sisters. The girls looked blankly around.

"She was just here," replied Connie.

"Maybe she went behind the house," said Rita. Twila ran around the house, with Marilyn right on her heels, but found the backyard empty.

Marilyn turned to Suzanne, who had also come along to investigate. "Run in and tell Mother we can't find Tanisha. See if she's in there. I'm going to check the playhouse, and Twila, why don't you look down by the chicken house?"

The girls scattered. When she heard someone call that Tanisha had not gone into the house, Twila felt a surge of panic. Where could she be? How could she have disappeared so fast? They were always so careful that someone knew where Tanisha was, and now in a moment of laxness she had just vanished.

On a whim, Twila decided to run down the woods trail. Maybe she had gone back in the woods or taken a notion to go the Grahams. Who knew what sort of scheme had been cooked in that little head of hers? Partway down the trail, she met Tanisha on the bike. Her cheeks were flushed from exertion, and her eyes were bright.

"Where were you?" Twila asked. She was too relieved to be angry.

"Oh," Tanisha replied cheerfully, "I decided to ride the trail and see how long it took me to go around the loop. This trail is so smooth I can ride really fast!"

"Well, come to the house now," said Twila, feeling rather weak. She was very glad Tanisha was okay and that her running off was innocent of any misbehavior. Twila led Tanisha up to the house, and the two of them explained to Mother and the rest of their worried sisters where she had gone.

"Well," said Mother briskly, "you may keep riding bike for a while, but I want you to stay *on* the driveway."

"Yes, Mother," said Tanisha cheerfully, and went to do as she was told.

"That was my fault," Mother admitted to the girls later. "I forgot all about specifying *where* Tanisha was to ride her bike. I guess I just assumed she'd know what I meant. I'm thankful that Tanisha has done well enough lately not to take advantage of my moment of carelessness!"

One day when the peas were nearly finished, Mother asked Suzanne, Connie, and Rita to pick the last of the peas and pull the plants to be fed to the chickens. "Twila, are you about finished with that pillow? When you're done, I want you to go help the younger girls."

Twila finished the last seam on the pillow she had started the day Uncle Noahs had come for a visit. She snipped all the stray threads and then smoothed the pillow with her hands. It wasn't perfect, but she was satisfied. Marilyn came and looked over her shoulder at the finished project. "So you got it all done? It looks nice! What are you going to do with it?"

"I thought about using it as a couch cushion, but the little children will drag it around and make it ugly. I'm going to put it on my bed so it stays nice." Twila put the scissors and pins away and then carried the pillow to the bedroom she and Marilyn shared and propped it against the other pillows on the bed. After one last look of satisfaction, she went outside and joined her younger sisters under the tree. She looked dubiously at the bowl of bulging yellowish pea pods Suzanne gave her and exclaimed, "These peas are so old, they aren't even worth shelling! They'll taste horrible."

Connie shrugged. "Mother said we were supposed to shell them. She wants them for supper tonight."

"Well, Mother's not going to want these great big ones," said Twila, and she sorted out the biggest ones and threw them away. Even so, when they were done shelling the remaining peas, they didn't look very appetizing. And when Mother went to cook them for supper, she was surprised.

"I guess they were more mature than I realized. But since you girls went to all the bother of shelling them, I'll sort out the best ones and we'll eat them anyway," she said.

Dad came home and they sat down to eat supper. Steaming bowls of pizza casserole and peas were passed around the table. The peas reached Rita, and she took a small spoonful. She ate her casserole, and then all that was left was her small pile of green marble-like peas. She stared at them a moment, and then looking up, she said solemnly, "These peas are very obese!"

The other girls laughed, and Dad grinned. "Well, I guess that's one way to say it!"

Robbie shoveled another bite of the starchy vegetables into his mouth and said happily, "I like 'em!"

The busy days of summer slipped by, and Twila thought it was nearly perfect. There were visits with church friends and a Hammond family gathering. The Hammond gatherings were getting so big now that it was getting harder and harder to be all together. An older cousin got married that summer, and another one was planning to get married in the fall. Marilyn and Twila were sure that wedding plans were in the near future for Sue as well, if the glow in her eyes was any indication.

One week Dad announced that the whole family was going camping, Tanisha included. They packed up and spent several days at a campground about an hour's drive away. One day they left the campground and went to visit a petting zoo. It was geared for smaller children, and the older girls didn't get much enjoyment out of it. But it was fun to watch the delight of the younger ones, especially Robbie and Tanisha.

There were also picnics back in the woods, visits with the Grahams, and lively discussions and friendly arguments with Jeff on the evenings he ate supper with them.

And of course, there was the never-ending work that came with summer. But Twila was apparently growing up more than she thought, for she found that she no longer minded work as much as she used to. She was sure she no longer daydreamed as much, either. She found it hard to believe that she was going to be fifteen in the fall. In some ways, she eagerly looked forward to it, for then she would be old enough to attend church youth functions with Marilyn and Jeff. After that, she would be getting her driver's license. It all seemed so grown-up. It was both scary and exciting at the same time.

"I think the most exciting thing about this summer is watching Tanisha's progress," Twila told Marilyn one evening. They had gone out after dark and were sitting on the lawn to watch the northern lights, something they rarely saw in Wisconsin.

Marilyn gasped as an especially lovely display of lights flashed across the sky and then said, "I know! She's becoming a dear and much-loved little sister. I used to be scared that Mother and Dad would adopt her, but now I keep holding my breath for fear something will come up that we won't be able to!"

The Hammond family kept hoping that soon Tanisha would be part of the family in name as well as in their hearts, but somehow, whenever it seemed that they would soon be able to finalize Tanisha's adoption, there was always a delay that put it off a little longer. But recently they had gotten the good news that they finally had a court date for September 15. On this day they would go before the judge, and Dad and Mother would sign the papers making Tanisha an official part of the family.

The flashes of northern lights were coming less and less. Twila flopped on her back and gazed at the star-studded sky. She absently picked out the Big and Little Dippers as her mind continued to ponder the situation with Tanisha. "You know," she said, breaking a long moment of silence, "if you compare Tanisha with other children her age, she really isn't doing all that well. She's got a long way to go before she catches up with them emotionally. But when I think of how she used to be and how she's doing now, it's like the difference between night and day! I just want to keep saying, 'Thank You, God! Thank You!' "

One beautiful sunny morning, Tanisha, Connie, and Rita decided to play dolls. Collecting their dolls, they sat down on the back steps of the house.

"Let's sing the Raggedy Ann song," suggested Rita. With girlish sweetness, their voices blended together as they sang.

> *A little girl was playing with Raggedy Ann one day*
> *When with such sweet delight I could hear her say,*
>
> *Her heart says I love you, her heart says I love you.*
> *Mommy, you know what? Her heart says I love you.*
>
> *Little girls just seem to know that Jesus loves them so.*
> *Now sometimes while at play this is what she says,*
>
> *My heart says I love You, my heart says I love You.*
> *Jesus, You know what? My heart says I love You.*
>
> *Lord, may I learn by listening as I hear her praises ring.*
> *That with this same sweet freedom my heart too can say,*
>
> *My heart says I love You. My heart says I love You.*
> *Jesus, You know what? My heart says I love You.*[8]

---

8 Author Unknown.

Tanisha jumped up, tucked her dolly under her arm, and ran to Mother, who was helping Twila weed flower beds nearby. She laid a small hand over her heart, and deliberately changing the words just a little, she sang, "My heart says I love you, my heart says I love you! Mother, you know what? My heart says I love you!"

Tears ran down Mother's cheeks, and she gathered the little girl into her arms and hugged her tight. "And my heart says I love you too!" Mother said softly as she held Tanisha close.

As Twila watched, she felt her own eyes fill with tears. Truly, she was witnessing a miracle! This little girl who had come to them wounded, neglected, and abandoned, her heart filled with anger and fear, was now slowly learning to love and trust. She was beginning to bloom like the flowers Twila and Mother were weeding.

The progress was slow, and there were many setbacks. But Tanisha was healing. At last her heart was able to say, "I love you!"

Acknowledgments

A heartfelt thank-you to my mom and sisters for their help with this book.

Thank you, Mom, for helping me plan the story line and for letting me use the same characters in this story that you used over two decades ago in writing the *Hammond Cousins* series. You also helped with the writing and editing.

Thank you, sisters, for listening and giving me ideas and for telling me what was typical of teenage girls when my own girls were little. Sheila, I want to thank you especially for the long hours you put in helping me with editing. I am so grateful for all you did!

I also want to say a big thank-you to the moms of children diagnosed with reactive attachment disorder who helped me with this book. You patiently answered my phone calls and e-mails as I tried to understand RAD and its effects on children. You gave me real-life incidents and allowed me to use them in the book. Your encouragement, support, and prayers meant so much to me. I cannot thank you enough.

Perhaps one of the most special e-mails I received in answer to my many questions was from an eleven-year-old child with attachment difficulties. Her mom gave her my questions and she answered. I treasure that e-mail. Thank you, Bethany!

I want to express my appreciation to my Christian Light editor, Carol Peachey Martin, for your help with this book. Your experience as an adoptive mom and your love and compassion for the children of trauma made you the perfect editor for this book. Thank you for taking what I wanted to say and making it sound better.

I can't forget to say thank you to my brothers and sisters, my children, and my and my husband's nieces and nephews for providing the happy family scenes and humor for this book. Somehow, my childhood memories and the real lives of the children around me kept creeping onto the pages of this book. You added love and laughter when the pain and grief of RAD became too heavy.

Thank you to my dear husband Craig for willingly walking the path of adoption with me. You quietly supported me in writing this book and believed that it could be done. And to my children, I thank you for teaching me to think outside the box. I admire your courage and resilience in the midst of the tough things in life. I feel immeasurably blessed to call you mine!

Most of all I want to say thank You to God who has adopted me and made me His child. He gave me words to write when I didn't know how to say it. His hand at my shoulder nudged me forward to finish this project.

Reactive Attachment Disorder

Attachment as a clinical term is a deep connection established between an infant and its mother or other primary caregiver that profoundly affects the child's emotional development and ability to build healthy human relationships. Normal bonding between parents and children happens naturally when pregnancy is uncomplicated, the child is anticipated, and the infant receives proper nourishment, love, and care from birth.

Reactive attachment disorder (RAD) may occur in babies or young children who lack the opportunity to connect in normal, healthy ways with their mothers or caregivers. Some causes of RAD are abuse (emotional, physical, or sexual), separation from the biological mother or a primary caregiver within the first three years of life, orphanage life, multiple moves to different homes with different caregivers, or profound neglect. Attachment difficulties have even been linked to traumatic events that happened while the child was still in the womb. War, domestic violence, mental illness, and substance abuse by the biological mother can seriously impair the mother's ability to connect emotionally with her child and provide the care, comfort, and protection her baby needs.

When the child's basic needs for love, protection, comfort, and care are not met, he may become unable to form healthy, normal interactions with people. A child who has not developed a close, trusting relationship with her primary caregiver may exhibit a lack of appropriate emotion, violent outbursts that are seemingly unrelated to the present circumstances, and/or a baffling affinity for strangers while lacking the ability to bond with safe and reliable caregivers.

Babies who experience trauma, abuse, or profound neglect learn that they can't depend on the adults closest to them. To them, the world is a dangerous and frightening place. They learn to cope with life in various ways, depending on their circumstances and personalities. Sometimes they withdraw emotionally from human interactions. Some become hypervigilant and unusually aware of their surroundings in an effort to control what happens to them. Often they display extreme frustration and anger toward caregivers who attempt to give the comfort and care that was lacking from their birth mothers; it upsets their habitual way of handling relationships.

A good attachment therapist can teach the family how to interact with the child in ways that nurture healthy bonding to its mother and other members of the immediate family. The child must learn that good things such as food, warmth, and comfort come from Mom. As he begins to trust parents who love him and care adequately for him, attachment grows. It is never too late to treat and repair a weak attachment, but the earlier the symptoms are identified and steps taken to repair them, the better.

Remember that God is the ultimate healer of broken emotions. He will guide committed parents to the tools they will need to nurture the emotionally needy children He has placed in their homes.

Christian Light is a nonprofit, conservative Mennonite publishing company providing Christ-centered, Biblical literature including books, Gospel tracts, Sunday school materials, summer Bible school materials, and a full curriculum for Christian day schools and homeschools. Though produced primarily in English, some books, tracts, and school materials are also available in Spanish.

For more information about the ministry of Christian Light or its publications, or for spiritual help, please contact us at:

ADDRESS :: P. O. Box 1212,
Harrisonburg, VA 22803
TELEPHONE :: 540-434-0768
FAX :: 540-433-8896
E-MAIL :: info@christianlight.org
WEBSITE :: www.christianlight.org

CHRISTIAN LIGHT
PUBLICATIONS